INSTRUCTOR'S MANUAL TO ACCOMPANY

# ESSENTIALS
## OF STATISTICS
### FOR THE BEHAVIORAL SCIENCES
#### SECOND EDITION

FREDERICK J. GRAVETTER
STATE UNIVERSITY OF NEW YORK - BROCKPORT

◆

LARRY B. WALLNAU
STATE UNIVERSITY OF NEW YORK - BROCKPORT

WEST PUBLISHING COMPANY
MINNEAPOLIS/ST. PAUL    NEW YORK    LOS ANGELES    SAN FRANCISCO

**WEST'S COMMITMENT TO THE ENVIRONMENT**

In 1906, West Publishing Company began recycling materials left over from the production of books. This began a tradition of efficient and responsible use of resources. Today, up to 95% of our legal books and 70% of our college texts and school texts are printed on recycled, acid-free stock. West also recycles nearly 22 million pounds of scrap paper annually—the equivalent of 181,717 trees. Since the 1960s, West has devised ways to capture and recycle waste inks, solvents, oils, and vapors created in the printing process. We also recycle plastics of all kinds, wood, glass, corrugated cardboard, and batteries, and have eliminated the use of Styrofoam book packaging. We at West are proud of the longevity and the scope of our commitment to the environment.

Production, Prepress, Printing and Binding by West Publishing Company.

TEXT IS PRINTED ON 10% POST CONSUMER RECYCLED PAPER

PRINTED WITH SOY INK™

# CONTENTS

# SECTION I: EXAM ITEMS

# CHAPTER 1
# INTRODUCTION TO STATISTICS

Multiple-Choice Questions

1.  Although research questions typically concern a
    _____, a research study typically examines a
    _____.
    a.   sample, population
    b.   statistic, sample
    *c.  population, sample
    d.   parameter, population

2.  The relation between a statistic and a sample is the
    same as the relation between
    *a.   parameter and population
    b.   dependent variable and independent variable
    c.   descriptive statistics and inferential statistics
    d.   operational definition and hypothetical construct

3.    Statistical methods that use sample data to answer
      general questions about a population are called
          a.    parameter
          b.    statistic
          c.    descriptive statistics
       *d.    inferential statistics

4.    Statistical techniques that summarize, organize, and
      simplify data are classified as _____.
          a.    population statistics
          b.    sample statistics
       *c.    descriptive statistics
          d.    inferential statistics

5.    The average score for an entire population would be an
      example of a _____.
       *a.    parameter
          b.    statistic
          c.    variable
          d.    constant

6.    A selection process that ensures that each individual
      has an equal chance of being selected is called
      _____ sampling.
       *a.    random
          b.    constant
          c.    variable
          d.    equivalent

7.   A college dean used the results from a student
     evaluation questionnaire to rank the faculty in the
     psychology department.  This is an example of
     measurement on a(n) _____ scale of measurement.
     a.   nominal
     *b.  ordinal
     c.   interval
     d.   ratio

8.   Determining a person's reaction time would involve
     measurement on a(n) _____ scale of measurement.
     a.   nominal
     b.   ordinal
     c.   interval
     *d.  ratio

9.   Determining a person's social security number would
     involve measurement on a(n)_____ scale of measurement.
     *a.  nominal
     b.   ordinal
     c.   interval
     d.   ratio

10.  After measuring a set of individuals, a researcher
     finds that Bob's score is three times greater than
     Jane's score.  These measurements must come from a(n)
     _____ scale.
     a.   nominal
     b.   ordinal
     c.   interval
     *d.  ratio

11.  In an experiment, the researcher manipulates the _____
     variable and measures changes in the _____ variable.
     a.  population, sample
     b.  sample, population
     *c.  independent, dependent
     d.  dependent, independent

12.  Which of the following is not a continuous variable?
     a.  time to solve a problem
     b.  temperature
     c.  height
     *d.  number of children in a family

13.  An operational definition is used to _____ a
     hypothetical construct.
     a.  define
     b.  measure
     *c.  define and measure
     d.  none of the above

14.  A researcher observed that preschool children playing
     in a red room showed more aggression than children
     playing in a blue room.  For this study, what is the
     independent variable?
     a.  preschool children
     *b.  color of the room
     c.  amount of aggression
     d.  the childrens' play

15. A recent study with college students reports that reaction times in the morning are faster than reaction times in the afternoon. For this report, reaction time is the

    a.  independent variable
    *b. dependent variable
    c.  population parameter
    d.  sample statistic

Questions 16 through 19 refer to the following set of scores (X values): 3, 0, 5, 2

16. For these data, what is $\Sigma X^2$ ?

    a.  20
    *b. 38
    c.  100
    d.  400

17. For these data, what is $\Sigma X + 2$ ?

    *a. 12
    b.  18
    c.  20
    d.  32

18. For these data, what is $\Sigma(X + 1)^2$ ?

    a.  61
    *b. 62
    c.  101
    d.  196

19. For these data, what is $(\Sigma X)^2$ ?

    a.  20
    b.  38
    *c. 100
    d.  400

20. How would the following mathematical operation be expressed in summation notation?

"Subtract one point from each score and find the sum of the resulting values."

   a.  $\Sigma X - 1$
*b.  $\Sigma(X - 1)$
   c.  $1 - \Sigma X$
   d.  $\Sigma(1 - X)$

21. How would the following mathematical operation be expressed in summation notation?

"Add two points to each score, square the resulting value, then find the sum of the squared numbers."

   a.  $\Sigma X + 2^2$
   b.  $(\Sigma X + 2)^2$
*c.  $\Sigma(X + 2)^2$
   d.  $\Sigma X^2 + 2$

22. A set of N = 4 scores has $\mu$ = 5. If the first three scores are X = 4, X = 6, and X = 7, what is the fourth score?

*a.  3
   b.  4
   c.  5
   d.  cannot be determined from the information given


### True-False Questions

T    1.    A summary value, usually numerical, that describes a population is called a parameter.

T    2.    A recent report concludes that subjects given a diet containing oat bran had lower cholesterol levels that subjects on a similar diet without oat bran.  For this study, cholesterol level is the dependent variable.

F    3.    The goal of "inferential statistics" is to simpify, summarize, and organize data.

F    4.    To establish a cause-and-effect relation between two variables, a researcher should use the correlational research method.

T    5.    In the experimental method, the researcher manipulates the independent variable.

F    6.    The reading ability of 2nd-grade students is classified as high, medium, or low.  This classification involves measurement on a nominal scale.

F    7.    A discrete variable must be measured on a nominal or an ordinal scale.

F    8.    Last week the three major networks were ranked as follows:  CBS first, NBC second, and ABC third.  This is an example of measurement on a nominal scale.

T    9.    Determining the number of students in each psychology course would be an example of measurement on a ratio scale.

T    10.    Determining the number of students in each psychology course would be an example of measurement of a discrete variable.

T    11.  Reaction time is an example of a continuous variable.

T    12.  A researcher records the sex of each child born in the county hospital during the month of June.  This researcher is measuring a discrete variable.

T    13.  If a researcher measures two individuals on a nominal scale, it is impossible to determine which individual has the larger score.

F    14.  In statistical notation, a lower-case letter $\underline{n}$ is used to identify the number of scores in a population.

F    15.  To compute $\Sigma X + 3$, you first add 3 points to each score and then find the sum of the resulting values.

T    16.  To compute $(\Sigma X)^2$, you first sum the scores and then square the total.

F    17.  For any set of scores, $\Sigma X^2 = (\Sigma X)^2$.

F    18.  For any set of scores, $\Sigma X + 2 = \Sigma(X + 2)$

## Additional Questions and Problems

1.  Statistical techniques are classified into two major categories:  Descriptive and Inferential.  Describe the general purpose of each category.

2.  Define the concept of "sampling error."  Note:  Your definition should include the concepts of sample, population, statistic, and parameter.

3. Calculate each value requested for the following set of scores. Scores: 1, 2, 3, 0, 4
   a. $\Sigma X$
   b. $\Sigma X^2$
   c. $(\Sigma X)^2$

4. Calculate each value requested for the following set of scores. Scores: 0, 1, 4, 3
   a. $\Sigma X + 2$
   b. $\Sigma(X + 2)$
   c. $\Sigma(X + 2)^2$

5. Calculate each value requested for the following set of scores.

   | | | X | Y |
   |---|---|---|---|
   | a. | $\Sigma X$ | 1 | 3 |
   | b. | $\Sigma Y$ | 3 | -2 |
   | c. | $\Sigma X \Sigma Y$ | 0 | 1 |
   | d. | $\Sigma XY$ | 2 | -4 |

## Answers to Additional Problems

1. The purpose of descriptive statistics is to simplify the organization and presentation of data. The purpose of inferential statistics is to use the limited data from a sample as the basis for making general conclusions about the population.

2. A <u>parameter</u> is a value that is obtained from a <u>population</u> of scores and is used to describe the population. A <u>statistic</u> is a value obtained from a <u>sample</u> and used to describe the sample. Typically it is impossible to obtain measurements for an entire population, so researchers must rely on information

from samples; that is, researchers use statistics to obtain information about unknown parameters. However, sample statistics are usually not identical to their corresponding population parameters. The error or discrepancy between a statistic and the corresponding parameter is called sampling error.

3.  a.   10
    b.   30
    c.   $(10)^2 = 100$


4.  a.   10
    b.   16
    c.   74


5.  a.    6
    b.   -2
    c.  -12
    d.  -11

# CHAPTER 2
# FREQUENCY DISTRIBUTIONS

Multiple-Choice Questions

Questions 1 through 4 concern the following table.

| X | f |
|---|---|
| 10 | 5 |
| 9 | 7 |
| 8 | 6 |
| 7 | 3 |
| 6 | 2 |
| 5 | 0 |
| 4 | 2 |

1.  For these data, N =
    - a.  7
    - b.  6
    - *c.  25
    - d.  cannot be determined from the table

2.  The percentage of scores with X = 8 is
    - *a.  24%
    - b.  32%
    - c.  60%
    - d.  14%

3. The proportion associated with X = 6 is
   a. 0.14
   b. 0.28
   *c. 0.08
   d. 0.02

4. For these data, $\Sigma X$ is
   a. 49
   b. 45
   *c. 202
   d. cannot be determined from the table

5. A distribution consists of the following scores:
   25, 26, 24, 26, 25, 3, 7, 6, 15, 7, 25, 24, 26
   The shape of this distribution is:
   a. symmetrical
   b. positively skewed
   *c. negatively skewed
   d. cumulative

6. For the class interval of 50-59, the real limits are
   a. 50 and 59
   b. 50.5 and 58.5
   *c. 49.5 and 59.5
   d. 50.5 and 59.5

7. Frequency distribution polygons are intended for use with
   *a. either interval or ratio scales of measurement
   b. only ratio scales
   c. either nominal or ordinal scales
   d. only nominal scales

8. A distribution of scores is being organized in a grouped frequency distribution table with an interval width of 10 points. If the lowest score in the distribution is X = 41, then the bottom interval in the table should be
   a.   40-50
   b.   41-50
   *c.  40-49
   d.   41-51

9. The width of the bars in a histogram is determined by
   *a.  the real limits of a score or class interval
   b.   the apparent limits of a score or interval
   c.   the frequency of a score
   d.   cumulative frequency

10. Which of the following statements is false regarding grouped frequency distribution tables?
    a.  An interval width should be used that yields about 10 intervals.
    b.  Intervals are listed in descending order, starting with the highest value at the top of the X column.
    c.  The lower apparent limit of each interval is a multiple of the interval width.
    *d. The value for N can be determined by counting the number of intervals in the X column.

11. On a graph, frequency is represented on the __???__ and values for scores are on the __???__ .
    a.  X axis/Y axis
    b.  horizontal line/vertical line
    *c. Y axis/X axis
    d.  class interval/horizontal line

12.  In a distribution with positive skew, scores with the highest frequencies are
   a.   on the right side of the distribution
*b.   on the left side of the distribution
   c.   in the middle of the distribution
   d.   represented at two distinct peaks


## True-False Questions

F   1.   In a frequency distribution table, the X column begins with the lowest score at the top and ends with the largest score at the bottom.

T   2.   The sum of the frequencies in a frequency distribution table must always equal N.

F   3.   In a frequency distribution table, the $\Sigma X$ may be obtained by simply adding the values in the column labeled X.

T   4.   If the lowest score in a distribution of N = 200 scores is X = 10 and the highest score is X = 50, then a grouped frequency distribution table should be used.

F   5.   The class interval, 15 - 19, has an interval width of four.

T   6.   In a grouped frequency distribution table, the bottom value in each class interval should be a multiple of the interval width.

F   7.   For a grouped frequency distribution table, a class
         interval should be omitted from the table if the data
         do not contain scores that lie within it.

F   8.   The class interval of 25 - 29 has apparent limits
         of 24.5 and 29.5.

T   9.   Bar graphs may be used for data that are measured
         on a nominal or an ordinal scale.

T   10.  A negatively skewed distribution has a tail on the
         left side of the graph.

F   11.  Frequency distribution polygons are best suited
         for data measured on a nominal scale.

T   12.  When listing scores in a frequency distribution
         table, you should not skip any scores, even if one has
         a frequency of zero.


## Additional Questions and Problems

1.  Briefly explain when and why you should use a grouped
    frequency distribution table instead of a regular
    table.

2.  Briefly explain what information is available in a
    regular frequency distribution table that is not
    available in a grouped table.

3.  For the following data, construct a grouped frequency
    distribution table. Include columns for proportion,
    and percent.
    ```
    41  32  67  44  46  47  36  53  56  45
    31  43  25  33  25  38  48  57  42  49
    ```

4.  For the following quiz scores, sketch a histogram of
    the frequency distribution.
    ```
    5   2  10   9   7   6  10
    7   8   5   7   8   4  10
    9   5   7   7   8   5
    ```

5.  For the following data
    a.  Which is more appropriate, a regular or a grouped
        frequency distribution table? Explain why.
    b.  Construct the appropriate table.
    c.  Based on the table, what is the shape of the
        distribution?
    ```
    23  36  16  15  27  41  30  13
    18  22  49  37  28  20  15  17
    34  45  35  24  16  12  28  31
    ```

## Answers to Additional Problems

1.  You should use a grouped table whenever the range of
    scores is too wide to list each value in a regular
    table. Usually, range of more than 15 points will
    require a grouped table.

2.  A regular table identifies each individual score
    exactly. However, in a grouped table, you simply know
    that an individual score is located in a particular
    interval, you do not know its exact value.

3.

| X | | f | P | % |
|---|---|---|---|---|
| 65 – 69 | | 1 | 0.05 | 5% |
| 60 – 64 | | 0 | 0 | 0% |
| 55 – 59 | | 2 | 0.10 | 10% |
| 50 – 54 | | 1 | 0.05 | 5% |
| 45 – 49 | | 5 | 0.25 | 25% |
| 40 – 44 | | 4 | 0.20 | 20% |
| 35 – 39 | | 2 | 0.10 | 10% |
| 30 – 34 | | 3 | 0.15 | 15% |
| 25 – 29 | | 2 | 0.10 | 10% |

4.

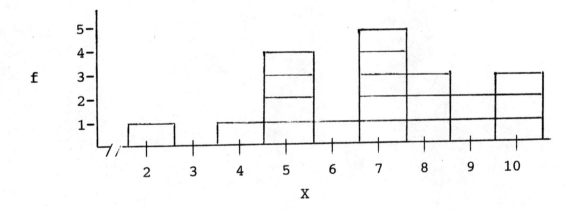

5.  a.  A grouped frequency distribution table would be
    better.  The lowest score is X = 12 and the highest is
    X = 49.  A regular table would require 38 rows.

    b.

    | X       | f |
    |---------|---|
    | 45 - 49 | 2 |
    | 40 - 44 | 1 |
    | 35 - 39 | 3 |
    | 30 - 34 | 3 |
    | 25 - 29 | 3 |
    | 20 - 24 | 4 |
    | 15 - 19 | 6 |
    | 10 - 14 | 2 |

    c.  The distribution is positively skewed.

# CHAPTER 3
# CENTRAL TENDENCY

## Multiple-Choice Questions

1.  In a sample of n = 6, five individuals all have scores
    of X = 10 and the sixth person has a score of X = 16.
    What is the mean for this sample?
    a.  $\bar{X}$ = 13
    *b.  $\bar{X}$ = 11
    c.  $\bar{X}$ = 13.2
    d.  Not enough information to find the mean

2.  A sample of n = 5 scores has a mean of $\bar{X}$ = 9.  What is
    $\Sigma X$ for this sample?
    a.  9/5 = 1.80
    b.  5/9 = 0.555
    *c.  5(9) = 45
    d.  cannot be determined from the information given.

3.  A sample of n = 25 scores has a mean of $\bar{X}$ = 11.  If
    each score in the sample is multiplied by 6, the new
    mean would be _____.
    a.   11
    b.    6
    *c.   66
    d.   150

4.  One sample of n = 4 scores has a mean of $\bar{X}$ = 10, and a second sample of n = 8 scores has a mean of $\bar{X}$ = 20. If the two samples are combined, the mean for the combined sample will be
    a.  equal to 15
    *b.  greater than 15 but less than 20
    c.  less than 15 but more than 10
    d.  none of the above

5.  A sample of n = 20 scores has a mean of $\bar{X}$ = 55. After one score is removed from the sample, the mean for the remaining scores is found to be $\bar{X}$ = 51. From this information you can conclude that the removed score was
    *a.  greater than 55
    b.  less than 55
    c.  it is impossible to estimate the magnitude of the score

6.  A teacher gave a reading test to a class of 5th-grade students and computed the mean, median, and mode for the test scores. Which of the following statements cannot be an accurate description of the scores?
    a.  the majority of the students had scores above the mean
    *b.  the majority of the students had scores above the median
    c.  the majority of the students had scores above the mode
    d.  all of the above must be false statements

7.  A distribution can have more than one
    a.  mean
    b.  median
    *c.  mode
    d.  none of the above

8.  For a distribution of scores, the mean is equal to the
    median.  This distribution is most likely to be _____.
    *a.  symmetrical
    b.  positively skewed
    c.  negatively skewed
    d.  impossible to determine the shape from the
        information given

9.  A set of individuals is measured on a nominal scale.
    To determine the central tendency for the resulting
    measurements, a researcher should use the
    a.  mean
    b.  median
    *c.  mode
    d.  it is impossible to determine central tendency for
        nominal measurements

10.  A distribution is positively skewed.  Which is the most
    probable order for the three measures of central
    tendency?
    a.   mean = 40, median = 50, mode = 60
    *b.   mean = 60, median = 50, mode = 40
    c.   mean = 40, median = 60, mode = 50
    d.   mean = 50, median = 50, mode = 50

11.  In a negatively skewed distribution of exam scores, Tom
    scored at the mean, Mary scored at the median, and Jane
    scored at the mode.  Who had the highest score?
    a.   Tom
    b.   Mary
    *c.   Jane
    d.   cannot be determined from the information given

12. What is the median for the following set of scores?
    Scores: 1, 3, 9, 10, 22
    a.  6
    *b. 9
    c.  9.5
    d.  11

13. What is the median for the following set of scores?
    Scores: 1, 4, 6, 17
    a.  4
    *b. 5
    c.  6
    d.  7

14. A population of scores has $\Sigma X = 60$ and a mean of $\mu = 12$. How many scores are in this population?
    *a. 5
    b.  12
    c.  60
    d.  cannot be determined from the information given

15. For any distribution, you can be sure that at least one individual has a score equal to the
    a.  mean
    b.  median
    *c. mode
    d.  all of the above

16. A positively skewed distribution has a mean of 80. If 10 points are added to each individual score, the new mean would be
    a.  80
    *b. 90
    c.  80 + 10/N
    d.  cannot be determined from the information given

17. The most commonly used measure of central tendency is

    *a.   the mean
     b.   the median
     c.   the mode
     d.   the range

18. Which of the following is a property of the mean?
     a.   changing the value of a score will change the
          value of the mean
     b.   adding a constant to each score will add the same
          constant to the mean
     c.   multiplying each score by a constant will
          multiply the mean by the same constant
    *d.   all of the above

19. A population of N = 10 scores has a mean of $\mu$ = 80.   If
    5 points are added to every score in the distribution,
    what is the value of the new mean?
     a.   still $\mu$ = 80
     b.   $\mu$ = 75
    *c.   $\mu$ = 85
     d.   $\mu$ = 130

20. For an extremely skewed distribution of scores the best
    measure of central tendency would be
     a.   the mean
    *b.   the median
     c.   the mode
     d.   central tendency cannot be determined for a
          skewed distribution

21. A distribution of N = 20 exam scores has a mean of $\mu = 50$. The instructor discovered that one student cheated on the exam so 20 points are subtracted from that student's score. What is the new mean for the class?

    a.  50

*b.  49

    c.  30

    d.  cannot be determined from the information given

22. The value of one score in a distribution is changed from X = 20 to X = 30. Which measure(s) of central tendency is certain to be changed?

*a.  the mean

    b.  the median

    c.  the mean and the median

    d.  the mode

## True-False Questions

T    1.  The purpose of Central Tendency is to find a single score that can serve as a representative value for an entire distribution.

F    2.  For any population of scores, $\Sigma X - \mu = 0$ .

F    3.  For a sample of n = 10 individuals, you can be sure that five individuals have scores below the mean and five have scores above the mean.

F    4.  A distribution with a mean $\mu = 50$ and a median of 70 probably is positively skewed.

T    5.  A distribution can have more than one mode.

T    6.    It is impossible to compute the mean for data that have been measured on a nominal scale.

F    7.    It is impossible to measure central tendency for data that have been measured on a nominal scale.

T    8.    For any symmetrical distribution the mean is equal to the median.

F    9.    On a 50 point exam Tom has a score of X = 23. This means that Tom scored below the median.

T    10.    A population has $\mu = 40$. If 5 points are added to every score, the mean will be changed to $\mu = 45$.

T    11.    The mean is often displaced toward the tail of a skewed distribution so that it is not a good, representative measure of central tendency.

F    12.    In addition to having two modes, a bimodal distribution typically has two medians.

F    13.    Adding a constant amount to every score in a population will not change the value of the mean.

T    14.    For a positively skewed distribution, the mean tends to have a larger value than either the median or the mode.

T    15.    After each score in a population is multiplied by 3 the mean is found to be $\mu = 90$. This means that the original mean was $\mu = 30$.

T    16.    In the behavioral sciences the most commonly used measure of central tendency is the mean.

T   17.  Extreme scores in a distribution are more likely
to affect the value of the mean than the value of the
median.

T   18.  The mode is the best way to measure central
tendency for data from a nominal scale.

T   19.  In a graph showing the relation between an
independent variable and a dependent variable, the
values of the independent variable are displayed on the
horizontal axis.

## Additional Questions and Problems

1.  What is the purpose for obtaining a measure of central
tendency?

2.  For the following set of scores, identify which measure
would provide the best description of central tendency
and explain your answer.
    Scores:  0, 30, 31, 33, 33, 34, 35, 37, 38.

3.  Describe two circumstances where the median would
provide a better measure of central tendency than the
mean.

4.  Although it was not discussed in the textbook, describe
what happens to the median and the mode when a constant
is added to every score in a distribution.

5.  In a class of N = 40 students, 21 people had scores of
X = 70 on an exam.  Explain why the median for this

set of exam scores must be located in the interval bounded by the real limits 69.5 and 70.5.

6. Find the mean, the median, and the mode for the set of scores in the frequency distribution table below.

| X | f |
|---|---|
| 5 | 2 |
| 4 | 3 |
| 3 | 2 |
| 2 | 2 |
| 1 | 1 |

Mean = _____

Median = _____

Mode = _____

7. Find the mean, the median, and the mode for the set of scores in the frequency distribution graph below.

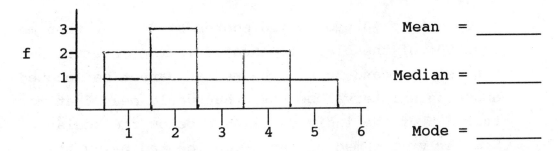

Mean = _____

Median = _____

Mode = _____

8. A set of n = 7 scores has a mean of $\bar{X}$ = 10. Another set of scores has n = 3 and $\bar{X}$ = 20. If these two sets of scores are combined, what is the mean for the combined group?

Answers to Additional Problems

1. The purpose of a measure of central tendency is to find the single score that best represents the entire distribution.

2.  The median would provide the best measure. Most of the scores are clustered between 30 and 38, so the "center" of the distribution should be in this range. However, the extreme score of X = 0 would displace the mean so that it is not representative.

3.  a.  When there are extreme scores (skewed distribution)
    b.  When there are undetermined scores.
    c.  When there is an open-ended distribution
    d.  When the data are measured on an ordinal scale

4.  When you add a constant to every score, the entire distribution is shifted to a new location. All of the individual scores are shifted, and the mean, median, and mode move along with the whole distribution.

5.  If 21 out of 40 people had scores of X = 70, then more than 50% of the class is located in the interval between 69.5 and 70.5. The median cannot be located above this interval because that would mean that more than 50% of the individuals were below the median. Similarly, the median cannot be located below this interval.

6.  Mean = 33/10 = 3.30.    Median = 3.5.    Mode = 4.

7.  Mean = 27/10 = 2.70.    Median = 2.5.    Mode = 2

8.  $\bar{X}$ = 13.

# CHAPTER 4
# VARIABILITY

## Multiple-Choice Questions

1.  The definitional formula for sum of squares is

    *a.   $\Sigma(X - \bar{X})^2$

    b.   $\dfrac{\Sigma(X - \bar{X})^2}{n}$

    c.   $\Sigma X^2 - \dfrac{(\Sigma X)^2}{n}$

    d.   $\Sigma X^2 - \dfrac{(\Sigma X)^2}{n-1}$

2.  In general, what is the relationship between the standard deviation and variance?

    a.   standard deviation equals the squared variance

    b.   variance is the square root of standard deviation

    *c.   standard deviation is the square root of variance

    d.   these two measures are unrelated

3.  A population of scores has $\mu = 50$ and $\sigma = 12$. If you subtract five points from every score in the population, then the value for the new standard deviation will be

    a.   7

    *b.   12

    c.   2.4

    d.   insufficient information, cannot be determined

4. The expression n - 1 is also known as
   a.  a biased estimate
   b.  a sum of squares
   *c.  degrees of freedom
   d.  the range

5. The measure of variability that is least likely to be greatly influenced by extreme scores is the ___???___.
   a.  range
   *b.  semi-interquartile range
   c.  variance
   d.  standard deviation

6. If a population has a mean of $\mu = 24$ with $\sigma = 4$ and $N = 10$, then $\Sigma(X - \mu)^2 = $ ___???___.
   *a.  160
   b.  16
   c.  2.5
   d.  400

7. What is the value of SS for the following set of scores?  5, 6, 1.
   a.  144
   b.  62
   *c.  14
   d.  none of the above

8. For the population of scores,  5  2  5  4  the variance equals
   a.  6
   b.  2
   *c.  1.5
   d.  1.22

9. Which set of scores has the least amount of variability?

    a.    11, 17, 31, 53

    b.    5, 11, 42, 22

    *c.   145, 143, 145, 147

    d.    27, 105, 10, 80

10. The correct formula for the sample standard deviation is

    a.  $\dfrac{SS}{n-1}$                      b.  $\dfrac{SS}{N}$

    *c.  $\sqrt{\dfrac{SS}{df}}$                d.  $\sqrt{\dfrac{SS}{N}}$

11. A population has $\mu = 40$ and $\sigma = 8$. If each score is multiplied by 2, the new standard deviation will be,

    a.    5

    b.    8

    *c.   16

    d.    insufficient information, cannot be determined

12. For a particular sample, the largest distance (deviation) between a score and the mean is 11 points. The smallest distance between a score and the mean is 4 points. Therefore, the standard deviation

    a.    must be less than 4

    *b.   must be somewhere between 4 and 11

    c.    must be greater than 11

    d.    it is impossible to say anything about the standard deviation

# True-False Questions

T    1.   When calculating SS, it is impossible to obtain a value less than zero unless a mistake is made.

F    2.   If a constant is added to every score in a distribution, then the standard deviation will increase by that constant.

F    3.   When computing sum of squares (SS) for samples, you must use n - 1.

F    4.   For any distribution, $\Sigma(X - \mu)^2$ will always equal zero.

T    5.   When variability is large among scores, the mean will be less representative of the scores in the distribution.

F    6.   If the values for several scores in the middle of a distribution were changed, then the range would be more affected than the standard deviation.

T    7.   A new score with a very extreme value is placed in a distribution.  It will influence the semi-interquartile range less than it will the range.

F    8.   The variance can be described as the average of the deviation scores.

F    9.   When computing the population variance, SS must be divided by n - 1.

T     10.   The symbol $s^2$ stands for the sample variance.

T     11.   By using n - 1 in the formula for sample variance, you will get an unbiased estimate of population variance.

F     12.   When you compute variance for a set of scores, you will get the same answer whether the scores comprise a sample or a population.


## Additional Questions and Problems

1.     A distribution of N = 10 scores has $\mu$ = 50 and $\sigma$ = 10. If another five individuals, all with scores of X = 50, are added to this distribution, what will happen to the variability - will it increase, decrease, or stay the same?  Explain your answer.

2.     Using the definitional formula, compute SS, variance and the standard deviation for the following population of scores.

          9   1   8   6

3.     Using the computational formula, compute SS for the following sample data.  Also use the data to compute the variance.

          4   3   6   4   8

4.     For the following sample data, compute the range and the variance.

          2   3   2   4   7   5   3   6   4

5.   For the following set of data, determine the semi-interquartile range.

|    |    |    |   |    |    |    |   |    |   |
|----|----|----|---|----|----|----|---|----|---|
| 8  | 8  | 10 | 7 | 9  | 6  | 11 | 9 | 10 | 7 |
| 11 | 11 | 7  | 9 | 11 | 10 | 11 | 8 | 10 | 7 |

6.   For the following set of data, compute the value for SS.

5   2   2   7   9

## Answers to Additional Problems

1.   The variability will decrease. Adding new scores at the mean will not change the mean, but it does result in more scores being clustered at the mean. As a result the variability (average distance from the mean) will decrease.

2.   SS = 38;   $\sigma^2$ = 9.5;   $\sigma$ = 3.08

3.   SS = 16;   $s^2$ = 4;   s = 2

4.   Range = 6;   SS = 24;   $s^2$ = 3

5.   Semi-interquartile range = 1.5

6.   SS = 38

# CHAPTER 5
# z-SCORES

<u>Multiple-Choice Questions</u>

1.  For a population with $\mu$ = 100 and $\sigma$ = 20, the z-score corresponding to X = 110 would be
    a.   +2.00
    *b.   +0.50
    c.   100/20
    d.   −0.50

2.  For a population with $\mu$ = 50 and $\sigma$ = 8, the X value corresponding to z = −0.50 would be
    a.   −4
    b.   49.50
    *c.   46
    d.   42

3.  A population of scores has $\mu$ = 44.  Within this population, an X value of 40 corresponds to z = −1. What is the population standard deviation?
    *a.   4
    b.   −4
    c.   1
    d.   cannot be determined from the information given

4.   A population of scores has $\sigma$ = 20.  Within this
     population, a score of X = 80 corresponds to z = -0.50.
     What is the population mean?
     a.   40
     b.   60
     *c.  90
     d.   cannot be determined from the information given

5.   A population has $\mu$ = 50 and $\sigma$ = 10.  If these scores
     are transformed into z-scores, the population of
     z-scores will have a mean of ___ and a standard
     deviation of ____.
     a.   50 and 10
     b.   50 and 1
     c.   0 and 10
     *d.  0 and 1

6.   A very bright student is described as having an IQ that
     is three standard deviations above the mean.  If this
     student's IQ is reported as a z-score, the z-score
     would be
     a.   $\mu + 3$
     b.   $\mu + 3\sigma$
     *c.  3
     d.   cannot be determined from the information given

7.   One advantage of transforming X values to z-scores is
     a.   all negative numbers are eliminated
     b.   the distribution is transformed to a normal shape
     c.   all scores are moved closer to the mean
     d.   all of the above
     *e.  none of the above

8.  A z-score of z = +2 corresponds to a location in the distribution that is
    a.   above the mean by two points
    b.   twice the mean
    *c.  above the mean by two standard deviations
    d.   two standard deviations above the lowest score

9.  A population distribution has $\mu$ = 80 and $\sigma$ = 6.  In this distribution a z-score of z = +2.00 identifies a location
    a.   two points above the mean
    b.   two points below the mean
    *c.  twelve points above the mean
    d.   twelve points below the mean

10. Suppose you earned a score of X = 53 on an exam. Which set of parameters would give you the highest grade?
    a.   $\mu$ = 50 and $\sigma$ = 3
    *b.  $\mu$ = 50 and $\sigma$ = 1
    c.   $\mu$ = 56 and $\sigma$ = 3
    d.   $\mu$ = 56 and $\sigma$ = 1

11. Suppose you earned a score of X = 40 on an exam.  Which set of parameters would give you the highest grade?
    a.   $\mu$ = 50 and $\sigma$ = 10
    b.   $\mu$ = 50 and $\sigma$ = 2
    *c.  $\mu$ = 45 and $\sigma$ = 10
    d.   $\mu$ = 45 and $\sigma$ = 2

12. Last week Tom had exams in Statistics and in English. He scored 10 points above the mean on both exams. From this information, you can conclude:

    a.   Tom has identical z-scores for the two exams
    *b.  Both of Tom's z-scores are positive
    c.   Tom will have a higher z-score for the exam with the lower mean.
    d.   None of the above

13. The mean for any distribution corresponds to a z score of

    *a.  0
    b.   1
    c.   N
    d.   cannot be determined from the information given

14. The median for any distribution corresponds to a z score of

    a.   0
    b.   1
    c.   N
    *d.  cannot be determined from the information given

15. For a symmetrical population with $\mu = 100$ the z-score corresponding to X = 120 would be

    a.   1.20
    b.   2.00
    c.   1.00
    *d.  cannot be determined from the information given

16. Using z-scores, a distribution with $\mu = 35$ and $\sigma = 8$ is being transformed into a new distribution with $\mu = 100$ and $\sigma = 20$. A score of $X = 39$ from the original distribution will be transformed into _____ in the new distribution.

   a.   $X = 104$

*b.   $X = 110$

   c.   $X = 120$

   d.   impossible to determine without more information

17. Using z-scores, a population with $\mu = 37$ and $\sigma = 6$ is transformed so that the new mean is $\mu = 50$ and $\sigma = 10$. How does an individual's z-score in the new distribution compare with his/her z-score in the original population?

   a.   new z = old z + 13

   b.   new z = (10/6)(old z)

*c.   new z = old z

   d.   cannot be determined with the information given

## True-False Questions

T    1.   In a distribution with $\mu = 50$ and $\sigma = 10$, a score of $X = 55$ corresponds to a z-score of $z = +0.50$.

F    2.   In a distribution with $\mu = 80$ and $\sigma = 20$, a z-score of $z = -1.00$ corresponds to an X value of $X = 79$.

T    3.   A positive z-score always corresponds to a score greater than the mean.

F    4.    Transforming X values into z-scores makes it possible to describe an entire distribution with a single number.

F    5.    In any population of scores, at least one individual will have a z-score of zero.

T    6.    The population mean <u>always</u> corresponds to a z-score of zero.

T    7.    If two scores come from the same population, the larger score will always have the larger z-score.

T    8.    If a distribution of scores is transformed into z-scores then the sum of the positive z-scores will be exactly equal to the sum of the negative z-scores.

T    9.    In a distribution with $\mu = 80$, a score of X = 110 correspoonds to z = +1.00. The standard deviation for this population is $\sigma = 30$.

F    10.    In a distribution with $\sigma = 8$, a score of X = 64 corresponds to z = -0.50. The mean for this population is $\mu = 60$.

T    11.    On an exam, Tom scored 8 points above the mean and had a z-score of +2.00. The standard deviation for the set of exam scores must be $\sigma = 4$.

F    12.    When any distribution of scores is transformed into z-scores exactly 50% of the z value will be positive and 50% will be negative.

T 13. If two individuals in a population have identical X scores, they also will have identical z-scores.

T 14. Transforming X values into z-scores will not change the shape of the distribution.

F 15. For any population, a z-score of +1.00 corresponds to a location exactly 10 points above the mean.

T 16. A negative z-score always corresponds to an X value that is less than the population mean.

T 17. Whenever a population is transformed into z-scores, $\Sigma z = 0$.

T 18. For any population, a z-score of +2.00 corresponds to a location above the mean by two standard deviations.

## Additional Questions and Problems

1. Describe the general purpose of a z-score.

2. Describe what happens to the mean, the standard deviation, and the shape of a distribution when all of the scores are transformed into z-scores.

3. For a population with $\mu = 50$ and $\sigma = 8$, find the z-score that corresponds to each of the following X values.

  X = 54  z = _____
  X = 52  z = _____
  X = 50  z = _____
  X = 38  z = _____

4. For a population with $\mu = 80$ and $\sigma = 16$, find the X value that corresponds to each of the following z-scores.

   $z = -1.50$    $X = \underline{\hspace{1cm}}$

   $z = +0.25$    $X = \underline{\hspace{1cm}}$

   $z = +2.00$    $X = \underline{\hspace{1cm}}$

   $z = -1.25$    $X = \underline{\hspace{1cm}}$

5. On a psychology exam with $\mu = 76$ and $\sigma = 12$, Tom scored at the mean, Mary had a score of $X = 73$, and Bill had a z-score of $z = -0.50$. Place these three students in order from lowest to highest score.

   $\underline{\hspace{3cm}}$  Student with lowest score

   $\underline{\hspace{3cm}}$  Student with middle score

   $\underline{\hspace{3cm}}$  Student with highest score

6. A set of exam scores are reported as X values and z-scores. On this exam a score of $X = 72$ corresponds to a z-score of $z = +1.00$ and a score of $X = 42$ corresponds to a z-score of $z = -2.00$. What are the values for the mean and standard deviation for this exam? (Hint: Sketch a distribution and locate each of the z-score positions.)

7. A population of scores with $\mu = 27$ and $\sigma = 4$ is transformed into a new population with $\mu = 100$ and $\sigma = 20$. What is the new value for each of the following scores from the original population?

   | original score | new value |
   |---|---|
   | $X = 19$ | $\underline{\hspace{1.5cm}}$ |
   | $X = 26$ | $\underline{\hspace{1.5cm}}$ |
   | $X = 31$ | $\underline{\hspace{1.5cm}}$ |
   | $X = 35$ | $\underline{\hspace{1.5cm}}$ |

# Answers to Additional Problems

1. The purpose of a z-score is to describe a location within a distribution using a single number.

2. When an entire distribution of scores is transformed into z-scores, the resulting distribution will have a mean of zero, a standard deviation of one, and the same shape as the original distribution.

3. $z = +0.50$

   $z = +0.25$

   $z = 0$

   $z = -1.50$

4. $X = 56$

   $X = 84$

   $X = 112$

   $X = 60$

5. Bill:  $X = 70$,  $z = -0.50$

   Mary:  $X = 73$,  $z = -0.25$

   Tom:   $X = 76$,  $z = 0$

6. $\mu = 62$ and $\sigma = 10$

7. $X = 19$ ----> $X = 60$

   $X = 26$ ----> $X = 95$

   $X = 31$ ----> $X = 120$

   $X = 35$ ----> $X = 140$

# CHAPTER 6
# PROBABILITY

## Multiple-Choice Questions

1.  A colony of laboratory rats contains 7 albino rats and
    23 hooded rats.  What is the probability of randomly
    selecting an albino rat from this colony?
    *a.    0.23
     b.    0.30
     c.    0.70
     d.    3.29

2.  An introductory psychology class has 9 freshman males,
    15 freshman females, 8 sophmore males, and 12 sophmore
    females.  What is the probability of randomly selecting
    a male from this group?
     a.    0.63
     b.    0.21
     c.    0.18
    *d.    0.39

3.  A jar contains 20 red marbles and 10 black marbles.  If
    you are take a random sample of n = 3 samples from this
    jar and the first two marbles are both red, what is the
    probability that the third marble also will be red?
     a.    18/30
    *b.    20/30
     c.    18/20
     d.    cannot be determined with the information given

4.  The proportion of scores in a normal distribution that
    corresponds to z-scores greater than +1.04 is ___???___ .
    a.    0.3508
    *b.   0.1492
    c.    0.6492
    d.    0.8508

5.  What proportion of the scores in a normal distribution
    is below z = 0.86?
    a.    0.3051
    b.    0.1949
    *c.   0.8051
    d.    0.6949

6.  What proportion of the scores in a normal distribution
    falls below z = -1.32?
    *a.   0.0934
    b.    0.4066
    c.    0.5934
    d.    0.9066

7.  What proportion of a normal distribution falls between
    z =  -1.16 and z = +1.16?
    a.    0.3770
    b.    0.6230
    c.    0.2460
    *d.   0.7540

8.  A normal distribution has a mean of $\mu = 40$ with $\sigma = 4$.
    What is the probability of sampling an individual with
    a score greater than 46?
    *a.   0.0668
    b.    0.4452
    c.    0.9332
    d.    0.0548

9.  A normal distribution has a mean of $\mu = 60$ with $\sigma = 8$.
    What is the probability of selecting an individual with
    a score greater than 54?
    a.   0.2266
    *b.  0.7734
    c.   0.7266
    d.   0.2734

10. A normal distribution has a mean of $\mu = 24$ with $\sigma = 3$.
    What score is needed to place in the top 14% of the
    distribution?
    a.   20.76
    *b.  27.24
    c.   25.08
    d.   24.42

11. A normal distribution has a mean of $\mu = 36$ with $\sigma = 4$.
    What proportion of the distribution falls between
    scores of $X = 30$ and $X = 38$?
    a.   0.3753
    *b.  0.6247
    c.   0.2583
    d.   0.7417

12. A distribution is normal and has $\mu = 90$ and $\sigma = 10$.
    What is the 64th percentile?
    a.   91.4
    b.   96.4
    c.   104
    *d.  93.6

13. For a normal distribution with $\mu = 90$ and $\sigma = 5$, what is the percentile rank for X = 84?

   *a.    11.51%

    b.    54%

    c.    38.49%

    d.    88.49%

14. For any normal distribution, the percentile rank for the mean will be

    a.    25%

   *b.    50%

    c.    34.13%

    d.    cannot be determined without additional information

## True-False Questions

F   1.  If there are 10 seniors and 40 juniors in a class, then the probability of randomly selecting one individual who is a senior is:  p(senior) = 1/4.

T   2.  A jar contains 15 red marbles and 75 blue marbles. If you randomly select a marble from this jar, the probability of obtaining a red marble is p = 15/90.

T   3.  For any normal distribution, scores that are below the mean always will have percentile ranks less than 50%.

F   4.  In random sampling, the requirement for sampling with replacement becomes much more important with very large populations.

F    5.   In a distribution of test scores, a score of X = 70 has a percentile rank of 54%. This means that 54% of the individuals received scores that are greater than X = 70.

T    6.   For a normal distribution, the semi-interquartile range can be obtained by multiplying 0.67 by the standard deviation.

T    7.   For any normal distribution, the mean and the median will have the same value.

F    8.   In any distribution, 80.64% of the scores fall between z-scores of +1.30 and -1.30.

T    9.   The Unit Normal Table can be used for any normal distribution, no matter what the values are for the mean and standard deviation.

T    10.  The value for a probability can never exceed 1.00, unless you have made a computational error.

F    11.  When determining the probability of selecting a score that is below the mean, you will get a negative value for probability.


## Additional Questions and Problems

1.   Describe the two conditions that must be satisfied for random sampling.

2.  For a normal distribution with $\mu = 43$ and $\sigma = 4$, find the following values:

    a.  the semi-interquartile range

    b.  the 33th percentile

    c.  the 93th percentile

    d.  the percentile rank for X = 50

3.  A normal distribution has a mean of $\mu = 61$ with $\sigma = 8$. Find the following probabilities:

    a)  $p(X > 66)$       c)  $p(X < 70)$

    b)  $p(X < 55)$       d)  $p(51 < X < 73)$

4.  A normal distribution has a mean of $\mu = 28$ with $\sigma = 5$. Find the scores associated with the following regions:

    a)  the score needed to be in the top 41% of the distribution

    b)  the score needed to be in the top 72% of the distribution

    c)  the scores that mark off the middle 60% of the distribution

## Answers to Additional Problems

1.  The two conditions for random sampling are:

    a.  Every individual has an equal chance of being selected.

    b.  If more than one individual is selected, the probabilities must remain constant after each selection.

2.  a.  Semi-interquartile range = 2.68

    b.  X = 41.24

    c.  X = 48.92

    d.  95.99%

3.  a.  $p = 0.2643$

    b.  $p = 0.2266$

    c.  $p = 0.8708$

    d.  $p = 0.8276$

4.  a.  $X = 29.15$

    b.  $X = 25.10$

    c.  $23.80 < X < 32.20$

# CHAPTER 7

# THE DISTRIBUTION OF SAMPLE MEANS

1.  When a random sample is selected from a population, the sample mean is not expected to be exactly equal to the population mean.  On average, the distance between the sample mean and the population mean is predicted by
    *a.   the standard error
    b.   the expected value
    c.   the mean of the population
    d.   the standard deviation of the population

2.  For a population with $\mu = 80$ and $\sigma = 20$, the distribution of sample means based on n = 16 will have an expected value of
    a.   5
    b.   15
    c.   20
    *d.   80

3.  For a population with $\mu = 100$ and $\sigma = 20$, the distribution of sample means based on n = 4 will have a standard error of

   a.   5
   *b.   10
   c.   20
   d.   100

4.  The standard deviation for the distribution of sample means is called

   a.   the expected value of $\bar{X}$
   *b.   the standard error of $\bar{X}$
   c.   the sampling value of $\tilde{\bar{X}}$
   d.   the standard $\bar{X}$

5.  The standard error of $\bar{X}$ provides a measure of

   a.   the maximum possible discrepancy between $\bar{X}$ and $\mu$
   b.   the minimum possible discrepancy between $\bar{X}$ and $\mu$
   c.   the exact amount of discrepancy between each specific $\tilde{\bar{X}}$ and $\mu$
   *d.   none of the above

6.  If two samples of exactly the same size are selected from the same population, then the two sample means will have

   a.   exactly the same expected value
   b.   exactly the same standard error .
   *c.   all of the above
   d.   none of the above

7.  As sample size increases, the expected value of $\bar{X}$

   a.   also increases
   b.   decreases
   *c.   stays constant

8.   The distribution of sample means
     a.   is always normal
     b.   cannot be normal unless the population
          distribution is normal
     c.   cannot be normal unless the sample size is greater
          than 30
     *d.  none of the above

9.   If you select a random sample of n = 16 scores from a
     population with $\mu$ = 50 and $\sigma$ = 8, how much error would
     you expect, on average, between the sample mean and the
     population mean?
     a.   zero, the sample mean should equal the population
          mean
     b.   0.5 points
     *c.  2 points
     d.   8 points

10.  A positively skewed population has $\mu$ = 50 and $\sigma$ = 20.
     A random sample of n = 4 scores obtained from this
     population has a mean of $\overline{X}$ = 55.   What is the z-score
     corresponding to this sample mean?
     *a.  0.50
     b.   0.25
     c.   2.00
     d.   cannot be determined because the population is not
          normal

11.  A normal population has $\mu$ = 30 and $\sigma$ = 4.   A random
     sample of n = 4 scores from this population has a mean
     of 32.   What is the z-score for this sample mean?
     a.   +0.50
     *b.  +1.00
     c.   +2.00
     d.   +4.00

12. A random sample of n = 4 scores is obtained from a normal population with $\mu$ = 20 and $\sigma$ = 4. What is the probabilty of obtaining a mean greater than $\bar{X}$ = 22 for this sample?

   a.  0.50
   b.  1.00
   *c.  0.1587
   d.  0.3085

13. For a normal population with $\mu$ = 80 and $\sigma$ = 20 which of the following samples is least likely to be obtained?
   a.  $\bar{X}$ = 90 for a sample of n = 4
   b.  $\bar{X}$ = 85 for a sample of n = 4
   *c.  $\bar{X}$ = 88 for a sample of n = 25
   d.  $\bar{X}$ = 84 for a sample of n = 25

14. Which of the following samples would have the largest standard error?
   a.  n = 25 scores from a population with $\sigma$ = 10
   *b.  n = 25 scores from a population with $\sigma$ = 20
   c.  n = 100 scores from a population with $\sigma$ = 10
   d.  n = 100 scores from a population with $\sigma$ = 20

15. A sample of n = 25 scores is determined to have a standard error of 2 points. What is the standard deviation for the population from which the sample was obtained?
   a.  2
   b.  2/5
   *c.  10
   d.  50

16. A random sample is selected from a population with $\mu = 80$ and $\sigma = 10$. To ensure a standard error of 2 points or less, the sample size should be at least

    a.  n = 5

    b.  n = 10

*c.  n = 25

    d.  it is impossible to obtain a standard error less than 2 for any sized sample

17. If sample size (n) is held constant, as the population variance increases the standard error will

*a.  increase

    b.  decrease

    c.  stay constant

    d.  cannot answer with the information given

## True-False Questions

F    1.  If a sample of at least 30 scores is randomly selected from a normal population, the sample mean will be equal to the population mean.

F    2.  According to the Central Limit Theorem, the Expected Value for a sample mean approaches zero as the sample size approaches infinity.

T    3.  It is possible for the distribution of sample means to be normal even if it is based on samples with less than n = 30.

F    4.  The mean of the distribution of sample means is called the standard error of $\overline{X}$.

T     5.   The standard error of $\bar{X}$ provides a measure of the distance, on average, between a sample mean and the population mean.

F     6.   To compute standard error for a specific sample mean, you simply find the difference between the sample mean and the population mean; that is, $\sigma_{\bar{x}} = (\bar{X} - \mu)$.

T     7.   The standard error will always be less than or equal to the standard deviation.

T     8.   If a sample consists of a single score ($n = 1$), the standard error is equal to the population standard deviation.

T     9.   The standard error of $\bar{X}$ can never be greater than the standard deviation of the population from which the sample is selected.

T     10.  The mean of the distribution of sample means will always be equal to the population mean.

T     11.  As sample size increases, the standard error decreases.

F     12.  On average, the difference between a sample mean and the population mean increases as the sample size increases.

T     13.  The standard deviation of the distribution of sample means is called the standard error of $\bar{X}$.

T     14.  On average, a sample of $n = 100$ scores will provide a better estimate of the population mean than would be obtained from a sample of $n = 50$ scores.

T    15.   Assuming that all other factors are held constant, as the population variability increases, the standard error will also increase.

F    16.   For a population with $\mu = 100$, you are more likely to obtain a sample mean greater than 110 with a sample of n = 100 than with a sample of n = 50.

F    17.   A sample of n = 16 scores is randomly selected from a population with $\mu = 80$ and $\sigma = 16$. If the sample mean is $\overline{X} = 84$, then the corresponding z-score is z = +0.25.

F    18.   A sample of n = 25 scores has a standard error of 2. This sample was selected from a population with $\sigma = 50$.

T    19.   In order to reduce the standard error by one-half, you must increase the sample size (n) by a factor of 4.

F    20.   If a random sample of n = 16 scores is obtained from a population with $\sigma = 20$, the sample mean is guaranteed to be within five points of the population mean.

T    21.   A researcher obtained $\overline{X} = 27$ for a sample of n = 36 scores selected from a population with $\mu = 30$ and $\sigma = 12$. This sample mean corresponds to a z-score of z = -1.50.

T    22.   If a sample mean corresponds to a z-score value near zero, then you can conclude that the sample mean is relatively close to the population mean.

1.  In words, define the "distribution of sample means."

2.  In words, describe what is measured by the standard error of $\overline{X}$.

3.  Describe the major differences between the following two distributions.
    a.  A population of scores with $\mu = 50$ and $\sigma = 6$.
    b.  The distribution of sample means based on samples of $n = 36$ selected from a population with $\mu = 50$ and $\sigma = 6$.

4.  For a population with $\mu = 80$ and $\sigma = 10$
    a.  How close, on the average, would you expect a sample of $n = 1$ score to be to the population mean?
    b.  How close, on the average, would you expect the mean for a sample of $n = 4$ scores to be to the population mean?
    c.  How close, on the average, would you expect the mean for a sample of $n = 25$ scores to be to the population mean?

5.  Each of the following samples was obtained from a population with $\mu = 50$ and $\sigma = 8$.  Find the z-score corresponding to each sample mean.
    a.  $\overline{X} = 54$ for a sample of $n = 4$
    b.  $\overline{X} = 46$ for a sample of $n = 16$
    c.  $\overline{X} = 48$ for a sample of $n = 64$

6. For a normal population with $\mu = 100$ and $\sigma = 12$
   a. What is the probability of obtaining a sample mean greater than 106 for a sample of $n = 4$ scores?
   b. What is the probability of obtaining a sample mean greater than 106 for a sample of $n = 16$ scores?

## Answers to Additional Problems

1. The distribution of sample means is the set of sample means obtained from all the possible random samples of a specified size (n) taken from a particular population.

2. The standard error of $\overline{X}$ is the standard deviation for the distribution of sample means, and it measures the Standard distance (or deviation) between a sample mean $\overline{X}$ and the population mean $\mu$.

3. The population consists of scores and the distribution of sample means consists of means (statistics). Although both distributions have the same mean, $\mu = 50$, the distribution of sample means has a standard deviation given by the standard error, $\sigma_{\overline{x}} = 1$. The distribution of sample means will be normal because the sample size (n) is greater than 30.

4. a. $\sigma = 10$
   b. $\sigma_{\overline{x}} = 5$
   c. $\sigma_{\overline{x}} = 2$

5. a. $z = +1.00$
   b. $z = -2.00$
   c. $z = -2.00$

6.    a.    z = 6/6 = 1.00    p = 0.1587
      b.    z = 6/3 = 2.00    P = 0.0228

# CHAPTER 8

# INTRODUCTION TO HYPOTHESIS TESTING

## Multiple-Choice Questions

1. A researcher risks a Type I error

   *a. anytime $H_0$ is rejected

   b. anytime $H_1$ is rejected

   c. anytime the decision is "fail to reject $H_0$"

   d. all of the above


2. By definition, a Type I error is

   a. rejecting a false $H_1$

   b. rejecting a false $H_0$

   *c. rejecting a true $H_0$

   d. failing to reject a false $H_0$


3. The probability of committing a Type I error

   a. is solely determined by the size of the treatment effect

   b. cannot be controlled by the experimenter

   *c. is determined by the level of significance that one chooses

   d. is determined by the value for beta ($\beta$)one selects

4.   The null hypothesis
     *a.   predicts that the treatment will have no effect
     b.   is denoted by the symbol $H_1$
     c.   is always stated in terms of sample statistics
          population parameters
     d.    all of the above

5.   The final step of hypothesis testing is to
     a.   locate the values associated with the critical
          region
     *b.   make a statistical decision about $H_0$
     c.   collect the sample data and compute the test
          statistic
     d.   state the hypotheses and select alpha

6.   The first step of hypothesis testing is to
     a.   locate the values associated with the
     b.   make a statistical decision about $H_0$
     c.   compute the test statistic for the sample
     *d.   state the hypotheses and select alpha

7.   A z-score that is used for hypothesis testing is also
     called a
     a.   critical region
     *b.   test statistic
     c.   critical value
     d.   level of significance

8.   In hypothesis testing, we assume that the distribution
     of sample means
     a.   is based on less than 30 means
     *b.   is normal
     c.   has a $\mu$ whose value is predicted by $H_1$
     d.   none of the above

9. One important assumption for hypothesis test with z-scores is that
   a. large alpha levels are used
   b. the value for beta be set prior to conducting the experiment
   *c. random sampling is used
   d. all of the above

10. A population is known to have a mean of $\mu = 45$. If a researcher predicts that the experimental treatment will produce a decrease in the population mean, then the null hypothesis for a one-tailed test would state
   *a. $\mu \geq 45$
   b. $\mu \leq 45$
   c. $\mu < 45$
   d. $\bar{X} \geq 45$

11. In hypothesis tests, standard error measures
   a. the size of the treatment effect
   b. variability among population means
   c. the size of the critical region
   *d. the expected difference due to chance between the sample data and population hypothesis

12. A critical region begins at $z = +1.96$ and $-1.96$. The obtained z-score for the sample data is $z = -1.90$. The correct statistical decision is
   a. fail to reject $H_1$
   *b. fail to reject $H_0$
   c. reject $H_1$
   d. reject $H_0$

13. A researcher expects a treatment to produce a increase in the population mean. Assuming a normal distribution, what is the critical z-score for a one-tailed test with $\alpha$ = .01?
   *a. +2.33
    b. ±2.58
    c. +1.65
    d. ±2.33

14. By selecting a smaller alpha level, a researcher is
    a. attempting to make it easier to reject $H_0$
    b. better able to detect a treatment effect
   *c. reducing the risk of a Type I error
    d. all of the above


## True-False Questions


F   1. Experiments are designed so that the experimenter's alternative hypothesis is supported when one fails to reject the null hypothesis.

T   2. If the null hypothesis is rejected when $\alpha$ = .01, then it would still be rejected for $\alpha$ = .05.

F   3. If the null hypothesis is rejected, then a Type I error has occurred.

F   4. When studying data from samples, you must state the null hypothesis in terms of sample statistics.

T   5. Alpha ($\alpha$) is the probability of committing a Type I error.

T    6.  It is easier to disprove a statement about the population than it is to prove it.

F    7.  In a Type II error, the experimenter concludes there is evidence for an effect when in fact an effect does not exist.

T    8.  Changing the level of significance from .01 to .05 increases the risk of a Type I error.

T    9.  When the z-score for sample data falls within the critical region, the decision is to reject $H_0$.

F    10. If one fails to reject $H_0$, then it has been proven that the null hypothesis is true.

F    11. To be certain that a treatment actually does have a real effect, a researcher should use a large value for alpha.

F    12. All other things being equal ($\mu$, $\sigma$, $\bar{X}$, and $\alpha$), you are more likely to make a Type I error with a sample of n = 4 than with a sample of n = 100.

F    13. If the null hypothesis is rejected using a one-tailed test, then it certainly would be rejected if the researcher had used a two-tailed test.

T    14. In a directional hypothesis test, the entire critical region is located in one tail of the distribution.

T    15. If a researcher is predicting that a treatment will increase scores, then the critical region for a directional test will be in the right-hand tail.

# Additional Questions and Problems

1. Define the "critical region" for a hypothesis test, and explain how the critical region is related to the alpha level.

2. The term "error" is used two different ways in hypothesis testing:
   a. Type I Error  (or Type II)
   b. Standard Error

   What can a researcher do to influence the size of the standard error?  Does this action have any effect on the probability of a Type I error?  What can a researcher do to influence the probability of a Type I error?  Does this action have any effect on the size of the standard error?

3. A researcher knows that the weights of 6-year olds are normally distributed with $\mu = 20.9$ kg and $\sigma = 3.2$.  She suspects that children in poverty-stricken regions are undernourished and therefore underweight.  With a sample of n = 16 children, the researcher obtains a sample mean of $\overline{X} = 18.2$.  Use a one-tailed test and the .01 of significance to determine if this sample is significantly different from what would be expected for the regular population of 6-year olds.

4.  A researcher investigates whether or not a new medication produces enough sedation to impair mental functioning. It is known that scores on a standardized test containing a variety of problem-solving task are normally distributed with $\mu$ = 64 and $\sigma$ = 8. A random sample of n = 12 subjects are given the drug and then tested. For this sample, the mean is $\bar{X}$ = 58. Does the drug impair mental functioning. Test with $\alpha$ = .01, one tail.

5.  Suppose reaction time for recognition of common words like "red" or "green" is normally distributed with $\mu$ = 225 milliseconds and $\sigma$ = 45. A psychologist would presents a sample of n = 20 subjects with a words that include names of colors. However, the color names are printed in a different color ink. That is, the word "red" might be printed in blue ink, or "green" might be printed in red. For these words, the sample had a mean reaction time of $\bar{X}$ = 261. Does presentation of color names in another color alter reaction time? Test with $\alpha$ = .01.

6.  A local school district recently implemented an experimental program for science education. After one year, 25 children in this special program obtained an average score of $\bar{X}$ = 93.4 on a national science achievement test. This test is standardized so that the national average is $\mu$ = 90 with $\sigma$ =14. Did the students in this special program score significantly above the national average? Use a one-tailed test with $\alpha$ = .05.

1.  The critical region consists of data that would be very unlikely if the null hypothesis is true. The value of alpha is used to define a precise probability for the term "very unlikely".

2.  The standard error can be decreased by increasing the sample size. Changes in sample size have no effect on the probability of a Type I error. However, the probability of a Type I error is under the direct control of the researcher who selects an alpha level for the test. The choice of an alpha level does not affect the standard error.

3.  $\sigma_{\bar{x}} = 0.8$ and $z = -3.38$. Reject $H_0$.

4.  $H_0$: $\mu \geq 64$. $H_1$: $\mu < 64$. The critical region is in the tail beyond $-2.33$. $\sigma_{\bar{x}} = 2.31$ and $z = -2.60$. Reject $H_0$.

5.  $\sigma_{\bar{x}} = 10.06$ and $z = +3.58$. Reject $H_0$.

6.  $H_0$: $\mu \leq 90$. $H_1$: $\mu > 90$. The critical region is in the tail beyond $z = 1.65$. The standard error is 2.8 and $z = 1.21$. Fail to reject $H_0$ and conclude that there is no evidence the program works.

# CHAPTER 9
# INTRODUCTION TO THE
# t STATISTIC

<u>Multiple-Choice Questions</u>

1.  Which of the following terms is not required when using the t statistic?
    a.  n
    *b.  $\sigma$
    c.  df
    d.  s or $s^2$ or SS

2.  If a researcher reports a t statistic with df = 21, how many individual subjects participated in the experiment?
    a.  n = 20
    b.  n = 21
    *c.  n = 22
    d.  cannot be determined from the information given

3.  If a sample consists of 16 individuals, then df for the t statistic for this sample would be
    a.  17
    b.  16
    *c.  15
    d.  cannot be determined from the information given

4.   With α = .05 the two-tailed critical region for a sample of n = 10 subjects would have boundaries of
     a.   $t = \pm 1.96$
     b.   $t = \pm 1.833$
   *c.   $t = \pm 2.262$
     d.   $t = \pm 2.228$

5.   With α = .01, the one-tailed critical region for a sample of n = 30 would have a boundary of
   *a.   $t = 2.462$
     b.   $t = 2.756$
     c.   $t = 2.457$
     d.   $t = 2.750$

6.   With α = .05, the critical values for a two-tailed z-score test are ±1.96.  The corresponding values for a two-tailed t test with α = .05 tend to be
     a.   less than ±1.96 (closer to zero)
   *b.   greater than ±1.96 (farther from zero)
     c.   also equal to ±1.96

7.   With α = .05 and df = 8, the critical value for a one-tailed t test is t = 1.860.  Assuming all other factors are held constant, if the df value were increased to df = 20, the critical value of t would
     a.   increase
   *b.   decrease
     c.   stay the same
     d.   not enough information to answer

8.  On average, what value is expected for the t statistic
    when the null hypothesis is true?
    *a.   0
     b.   1
     c.   1.96
     d.   t > 1.96

9.  The estimated standard error, $s_{\bar{x}}$, provides a measure of
    the "average" or standard discrepancy between
     a.   a score and the population mean (X and $\mu$)
    *b.   a sample mean and the population mean ($\bar{X}$ and $\mu$)
     c.   a score and the sample mean (X and $\bar{X}$)
     d.   none of the above

10. What is the estimated standard error for a sample of n
    = 9 scores with SS = 288?
     a.   96
    *b.    2
     c.    6
     d.   12

11. What is the estimated standard error for a sample of n
    = 9 scores with s = 12?
     a.   12/9
     b.   12/8
    *c.   $12/\sqrt{9}$
     d.   $12/\sqrt{8}$

12. For a sample of n = 15, what t values determine the
    two-tailed critical region for $\alpha$ = .05?
     a.   +1.761,   -1.761
    *b.   +2.145,   -2.145
     c.   +2.131,   -2.131
     d.   +1.753,   -1.753

13. Holding everything else constant, increasing sample size
    a.  decreases standard error
    b.  increases the magnitude of the t statistic
    c.  increases degrees of freedom
   *d.  all of the above

14. When n is small (less than 30), the t distribution
    a.  is identical in shape t the normal z distribution
   *b.  is flatter and more spread out than the normal z distribution
    c.  is taller and narrower than the normal z distribution
    d.  cannot be specified, making hypothesis tests impossible

15. An important assumption for the t test is that
   *a.  the population distribution is normal
    b.  the sample size be less than 30
    c.  the value for $\sigma$ is known
    d.  the t distribution is normal

16. Two samples from the same population both have n = 10 scores and both have $\bar{X}$ = 45. If t statistics are computed for these two samples, then
    a.  the two t statistics will be identical
    b.  the sample with the larger variance will produce the larger t statistic
   *c.  the sample with the smaller variance will produce the larger t statistic

17. Two different samples, each with n = 10 scores, are selected from the same population. If the two sample means are identical, then the two sample means will produce

*a. identical z-scores

 b. identical t statistics

 c. all of the above

 d. none of the above


## True-False Questions

T   1. With the exception of a hypothesized value for $\mu$, all of the information needed to compute a t statistic comes from the sample data.

T   2. When the value of $\sigma$ is not known, it is impossible to use a z-score for a hypothesis test.

T   3. The larger the sample size, the larger the df value for the t statistic.

F   4. Estimated standard error is computed from $\sigma$.

F   5. The t statistic uses $\sigma_{\bar{x}}$ in the denominator instead of $\sigma$.

T   6. The larger the value for df, the more a t distribution resembles a normal distribution.

T   7. The t distribution is symmetrical and has a mean of zero.

T   8. The smaller the value for df, the more flat and spread out the t distribution becomes.

T    9.  For any fixed value of $\alpha$, the critical values for the t statistic will move closer to zero as df increases.

F    10. Two separate samples, each with n = 30 scores, from the same population will produce identical t statistics if the two sample means are equal.

F    11. The t statistic is less versatile than the z-score for hypothesis testing situations.

T    12. An important assumption for the t test is that the population distribution is normal.

F    13. In general, an increase in the sample variance will produce an increase in the magnitude of the t statistic.

F    14. In general, a small value (near zero) for a t statistic, will result in rejecting the null hypothesis.

T    15. In general, an increase in the size of the difference between $\bar{X}$ and the hypothesized value for $\mu$ will produce an increase in the size of the t statistic.

F    16. The t distribution can be used for hypothesis tests only if n > 30.

F    17. A sample of n = 15 scores will produce a t statistic with df = 16.

# Additional Questions and Problems

1. Although you can compute a z-score for a sample of $n = 1$, it is impossible to compute a t statistic for a sample that has only one score. Explain why.

2. How does the shape of a t distribution compare with the normal distribution? How does the shape of a t distribution depend on sample size (n)?

3. Without some correction, sample variability is said to be "biased." Define the term biased, and explain how this bias is corrected in the formulas for sample variance and sample standard deviation.

4. A normal population has a mean of $\mu = 25$. After receiving a treatment, a sample yields the following data.

   > 20   28   20   20

   Is there evidence for a treatment effect? Use an alpha level of .05.

5. A sample of freshmen take a reading comprehension test. If the mean for the general population the mean on this test is $\mu = 12$, can you conclude that this sample is significantly different from the population. Test with $\alpha = .05$.

   > Sample Scores:   16, 8, 8, 6, 9, 11, 13, 9, 10

6. For an experiment, the null hypothesis predicts that $\mu = 28$. Do the following sample data support the conclusion that a treatment effect exists? Use the .05 level of significance.

   > Sample Data:   $\overline{X} = 24$,   $n = 9$,   SS = 128.

# Answers to Additional Problems

1.  Before you can find a t statistic, you must first compute the sample variance or standard deviation ($s^2$ or $s$).  With only one score, it is impossible to compute variability for the sample.

2.  The t distributions tend to approximate a normal shape, but they generally have greater variability (look flatter) than a normal distribution.  As sample size increases, the t distribution becomes closer to a normal shape.

3.  On average, sample variability is less than population variability.  Whenever a statistic consistently underestimates (or overestimates) the corresponding population parameter, the statistic is said to be biased.  The bias in sample variability is corrected by dividing by n - 1 (instead of n) in the formulas for sample variance and standard deviation.

4.  $H_0$: $\mu = 25$.  For these data, $\overline{X} = 22$, $s = 4$, and $t(3) = -1.50$.  Fail to reject $H_0$.

5.  For these data $\overline{X} = 10$ and SS = 72.  The standard error is 1 and $t = -2.00$.  Fail to reject $H_0$.

6.  For these data, $t(8) = -3.00$.  Reject $H_0$ and conclude that a significant treatment effect exists.

# CHAPTER 10
# HYPOTHESIS TESTS WITH
# TWO INDEPENDENT SAMPLES

## Multiple-Choice Questions

1.  One clue to identifying a situation calling for an independent measures t is
    a.   the value for σ should be known
    b.   the mean for a treated group of subjects is compared to a known population mean
    c.   one sample is used to test a hypothesis about one population
    *d.  there are two samples containing different subjects

2.  What is the pooled variance for the following two samples?
    Sample 1:  n = 6 and SS = 360.
    Sample 2:  n = 10 and SS = 480.
    a.   4
    b.   16
    *c.  840/14
    d.   840/16

3. What is the estimated standard error for mean differences for the following two samples?

        Sample 1: n = 6 and SS = 56
        Sample 2: n = 4 and SS = 40

    a. 5
  *b. $\sqrt{5}$
    c. 12
    d. 9.6

4. A researcher reports t(24) = 2.67 for an independent measures experiment. How many subjects participated in this experiment?

    a. 24
    b. 12
  *c. 26
    d. 23

5. An independent measures experiment uses two samples with n = 7 in each to compare two experimental treatments. The t statistic from this experiment will have degrees of freedom equal to

  *a. 12
    b. 6
    c. 13
    d. 9

6. The homogeneity of variance assumption states that
    a. the two sample variances are equal
    b. the two samples come from the same population
    c. variance must stay constant for each subject in the experiment
  *d. the two samples come from populations with equal variances

7. The alternative hypothesis for an independent measures t test states

    a. $\mu_1 - \mu_2 = 0$
    b. $\bar{X}_1 - \bar{X}_2 \neq 0$
*c. $\mu_1 - \mu_2 \neq 0$
    d. $\bar{X}_1 - \bar{X}_2 = 0$

Questions 8 through 10 refer to the following.
A researcher reports the statistical results of an independent measure t as "t(5) = -2.12, p > .05, two tails."

8. For this study, what critical regions were used?

    a.   +2.015 and -2.015
*b.   +2.571 and -2.571
    c.   +2.776 and -2.776
    d.   cannot be determined from the information given

9. What statistical decision was made?

*a.   the researcher failed to reject $H_0$
    b.   the null hypothesis was rejected
    c.   there was a marginally significant effect
    d.   cannot be determined from the researcher's statement

10. How many subjects participated in the study?

    a.   6
    b.   4
*c.   7
    d.   insufficient information given

11. What value should be expected for the independent
measures t statistic if the null hypothesis were true?
    a. 1.00
    *b. 0
    c. between +1.96 and −1.96
    d. none of the above

    Use the following data for questions 12 through 14.

| Treatment 1 | Treatment 2 |
|---|---|
| n = 6 | n = 6 |
| $\overline{X}$ = 10 | $\overline{X}$ = 14 |
| SS = 70 | SS = 50 |

12. For these data the independent measures t statistic has
degrees of freedom equal to
    *a. 10
    b. 5
    c. 12
    d. 11

13. For these data, the estimated standard error for sample
mean differences equals
    a. 4
    b. 12
    c. 120
    *d. 2

14. For these data the independent measures t statistic is
equal to
    a. −1.00
    *b. −2.00
    c. $-4/\sqrt{2}$
    d. $4/\sqrt{8}$

# True-False Questions

T     1. Two separate samples, each with n = 9, will produce an independent measures t statistic with df = 16.

F     2. Increases in sample variance will produce larger values for the t statistic.

F     3. Pooled variance is obtained by adding two SS values and dividing by 2.

T     4. The null hypothesis for the independent measures t test states that there is no difference between the two population means.

T     5. If one independent measures study has $n_1 = 7$ and $n_2 = 13$ and another study has $n_1 = 10$ and $n_2 = 10$, then both studies will have df = 18.

F     6. If other factors are held constant, the larger the estimated standard error of sample mean differences, the more likely you will obtain a t statistic in the critical region.

T     7. The independent measures t test uses data from two separate samples to test a hypothesis about the mean difference between two populations.

T     8. The only way to obtain a value of zero for the independent measures t statistic is when $\overline{X}_1 = \overline{X}_2$.

T     9. Homogeneity of Variance assumes that the two population variances are equal.

F       10.   The F-max test is used to determine if the two
population means are equal.


T       11.   All other things equal, the larger the difference
between the two sample means, the more likely it is
that an independent measures hypothesis test will
reject the null hypothesis.


F       12.   When pooling variances, the resulting value will
be closer to the variance from the sample with the
smaller n.


F       13.   The F-max test for homogeneity of variance
requires that you find the ratio of the smaller
variance over the larger variance.


F       14.   If a researcher reports that $t(6) = 1.98$, $p > .05$,
then $H_0$ was rejected.


T       15.   For an independent measures study, $H_1$ for a two-
tailed test states that $\mu_1 - \mu_2 \neq 0$.


T       16.   Considering two studies using an independent
measures design, it is possible for both studies to
have the exact same mean difference $(\overline{X}_1 - \overline{X}_2)$ yet
different values for their computed t.


## Additional Questions and Problems


1.   Describe the data that are collected for an independent
measures t test and the hypotheses that the test
evaluates.

2.  Explain why the homogeneity of variance assumption must
    be satisfied before you can interpret the results of an
    independent measures t test.

3.  The following data are from an independent measures
    experiment comparing two treatment conditions.  Do
    these data indicate a significant difference between
    the treatments at the .05 level of significance?

    | Treatment 1 | Treatment 2 |
    |:-----------:|:-----------:|
    | 13 | 9 |
    | 9 | 5 |
    | 7 | 5 |
    | 11 | 9 |

4.  A biopsychologist studies the role of the brain
    chemical serotonin in aggression.  One sample of rats
    serves as a control group and receives a placebo.  A
    second sample of rats receive a drug that lowers brain
    levels of serotonin.  Then the researcher tests the
    animals by recording the number of aggressive responses
    each of the rats display.  For the data below, is there
    a significant effect of the drug on aggression?  What,
    if any, role does serotonin have in aggression?  Use an
    alpha level of .05, two tails.

    | Low Serotonin | Control |
    |:-------------:|:-------:|
    | $n = 6$ | $n = 8$ |
    | $\bar{X} = 22$ | $\bar{X} = 14$ |
    | $SS = 108$ | $SS = 180$ |

5.  An educational psychologist studies the effect of frequent testing on retention of course material. In one of the professor's sections, students are given quizzes each week. The second section receives only two tests during the semester. At the end of the semester, both sections receive the same cumulative final exam. Is there a significant effect of testing frequency on retention? Use the .01 level of significance.

| Frequent Quizzes | Two Exams |
|---|---|
| $n = 5$ | $n = 5$ |
| $\bar{X} = 82$ | $\bar{X} = 68$ |
| $SS = 175$ | $SS = 145$ |

6.  The following data were obtained from an independent measures study. Determine if there is a significant difference between the treatments. Use $\alpha = .01$

| Treatment 1 | Treatment 2 |
|---|---|
| 5 | 6 |
| 1 | 10 |
| 2 | 14 |
| 3 | 12 |
| 4 | 18 |

Answers to Additional Problems

1.  An independent measures t statistic requires scores from two separate samples. The null hypothesis states that there is no difference between the means of the two populations (or treatments) from which the samples were obtained.

2. Before you can average (or pool) the two sample variances it is necessary that both samples are estimating the same population variance. Otherwise, the pooled value is meaningless. If the homogeneity assumption is violated, an extreme value for t could be caused by either:

   a. An incorrect value for $\mu_1 - \mu_2$ from $H_0$

   b. A meaningless value for the pooled variance. In this situation, you cannot conclude that an extreme t necessarily indicates that $H_0$ is wrong.

3. For treatment 1, $\overline{X} = 10$ and SS = 20. For treatment 2, $\overline{X} = 7$ and SS = 16. For these data the pooled variance is 6, the standard error is $\sqrt{3} = 1.73$, and the t statistic is $t(6) = 1.73$. Fail to reject $H_0$.

4. $H_0$: $\mu_1 - \mu_2 = 0$. For these data the pooled variance is 24, the standard error is 2.65, and the t statistic is $t(12) = 3.02$. Reject $H_0$. Lower serotonin levels cause an increase in aggression.

5. Pooled variance = 40, standard error = 4, $t(8) = 3.50$. Reject the null hypothesis.

6. For treatment 1, $\overline{X} = 3$ and SS = 10. For treatment 2, $\overline{X} = 12$ and SS = 80. Pooled variance = 11.25, standard error = 2.12, $t(8) = -4.25$. Reject $H_0$.

# CHAPTER 11
# HYPOTHESIS TESTS WITH
# RELATED SAMPLES

## Multiple-Choice Questions

1.  A repeated measures study would not be appropriate for which of the following situations?

    a.  A researcher would like to study the effect of practice on performance.

    *b.  A researcher would like to compare individuals from two different populations.

    c.  The effect of a treatment is studied in a small group of individuals with a rare disease.

    d.  A developmental psychologist examines how behavior unfolds with a longitudinal study.

2.  Which of the following studies uses a matched-subjects design?

    a.  A group of twins is tested for visual acuity on one day and then tested again the following day after receiving a drug.

    b.  A sample of children is tested for vocabulary skills at age six and then again at age ten.

    *c.  Subjects are assigned to one of two treatment groups so that each subject in one group has the same IQ as a subject in the other group.

    d.  none of the above

3.   What is the value of $\overline{D}$ for the following set of difference scores?

      Scores:   3, -8, 6, -4, -2

 *a.   -1

  b.   -5

  c.   23

  d.   23/5 = 4.6

4.   A repeated measures experiment and a matched subjects experiment both produce t statistics with df = 20. Which experiment used more subjects?

  a.   repeated measures

 *b.   matched subjects

  c.   they both used n = 21 subjects

  d.   they both used n = 22 subjects

5.   A researcher conducts an experiment comparing two treatment conditions and obtains 20 scores in each treatment.  Which design would require the smallest number of subjects.

  a.   an independent-measures design

 *b.   a repeated-measures design

  c.   a matched-subjects design

  d.   b and c

6.   What is the value of $s_{\overline{D}}$ for the following set of D-scores?

        4    8    4    4

  a.   12

  b.    2

  c.    4

 *d.    1

7. What is the value for $s_{\bar{D}}$ for a set of n = 9 D-scores with SS = 32?

    a.   32

  *b.   0.67

    c.   2

    d.   4

8. For the repeated measures t statistic, df = _____.

    a.  $n_1 + n_2 - 2$

    b.  $(n_1 - 1) + (n_2 - 1)$

  *c.  $n - 1$

    d.  $n_1 + n_2 - 1$

9. A repeated-measures experiment with a sample of n = 16 subjects would produce a t statistic with df = ____.

  *a.  15

    b.  16

    c.  30

    d.  32

10. With $\alpha = .05$ and a sample of n = 12 subjects in a repeated-measures experiment, the critical region for the related-samples t statistic has boundaries of

    a.  t = ±2.228

    b.  t = ±1.812

    c.  t = ±1.796

  *d.  t = ±2.201

11. If the null hypothesis is true, on average the expected value for the related-samples t statistic is

  *a.  0

    b.  1

    c.  1.96

    d.  t > 1.96

12. Which of the following sets of data is most likely to produce a significant t statistic?
   a.  $\bar{D}$ = 2 and SS = 10
   b.  $\bar{D}$ = 2 and SS = 100
   *c.  $\bar{D}$ = 10 and SS = 10
   d.  $\bar{D}$ = 10 and SS = 100

13. An advantage of a repeated-measures design is that it reduces the contribution of error variability due to
   a.  $\bar{D}$
   b.  degrees of freedom
   c.  the effect of the treatment
   *d.  individual differences

14. For the repeated-measures t test, $H_0$ states
   *a.  $\mu_D = 0$
   b.  $\bar{D} = 0$
   c.  $\mu_D \neq 0$
   d.  $\mu_D = \bar{D}$

15. For a repeated-measures experiment, df = 10. How many subjects were used in the entire study?
   a.   9
   b.  22
   c.  18
   *d.  11

16. One concern with a repeated-measures study is the possibility of
   a.  negative values for the difference scores
   *b.  carry-over effects
   c.  obtaining a mean difference that is due to individual differences rather than treatment differences
   d.  all of the above

F.  1.  For a repeated-measures design, separate samples are used for each treatment condition.

T   2.  With a repeated-measures design, it is possible to use one sample of subjects to evalate the difference between two treatments.

F   3.  When computing the difference scores (D values) for a repeated-measures study, always subtract the smaller score from the larger score so that the result is positive.

T   4.  The numerator of the repeated-measures t test formula uses the sample value, $\bar{D}$.

T   5.  Estimated standard error for a repeated-measures t statistic is based on the standard deviation of difference scores.

F   6.  For a repeated-measures design, df = $n_1 + n_2 - 2$ for the t statistic.

T   7.  The null hypothesis for a repeated-measures experiment predicts that $\mu_D = 0$.

T   8.  The repeated-measures t statistic can be used with either a repeated-measures or a matched-subjects design.

T   9.  Repeated-measures experiments reduce the variance contributed by individual differences.

F     10.   Repeated-measures designs are particularly well-suited to research questions concerning the difference between two distinct populations (for example, males versus females).

T     11.   If all other factors are held constant, an increase in the magnitude of $\bar{D}$ will cause an increase in the size of the t statistic.

F     12.   If all other factors are held constant, an increase in the variability of the D-scores will cause an increase in the size of the t statistic.

F     13.   One disadvantage of repeated-measures designs is that they typically require more subjects than an independent-measures design.

T     14.   A repeated-measures experiment and a matched-subjects experiment both produce t statistics with df = 20. The matched-subjects experiment used more subjects.

## Additional Questions and Problems

1.   Briefly explain the advantages and disadvantages of using a repeated-measures design as opposed to an independent-measures design.

2.    A teacher gives a third grade class of n = 16 a vocabulary test at the beginning of the school year. To evaluate the changes that occur during the year, students are tested again the end of the year. Their test scores revealed an average improvement of $\bar{D}$ = 5.7 points with $s^2$ = 144. Does this constitute a significant improvement? Use a one-tailed test with an alpha level of .05.

3.    For a sample of n = 25 high school students, the mean improvement in SAT scores following a preparatory course was $\bar{D}$ = 18 points with SS = 9600. On the basis of this sample, can you conclude that the preparatory course has a significant effect on SAT scores. Test at the .05 level of significance.

4.    A researcher would like to determine if relaxation training will reduce the number of headaches for chronic headache sufferers. For a week prior to training, each subject records the number of headaches suffered. Subjects then receive relaxation training and for the week following training the number of headaches is again measured. The change in number of headaches before and after training is as follows (minus signs indicate a reduction):

      -5    -1    -4    -3    -6    -8    0    +1    -1

      Is there an effect of training? Use $\alpha$ = .05

5. A therapist would like to determine if acknowledging positive statements and ignoring negative statements that a patient makes will have an effect on future statements. Before treatment, the therapist interviews patients and records the number of positive remarks made. During the next session, the therapist acknowledges every positive self-statement by a head nod or saying "yes, I agree," and ignores negative remarks. Then during the session after this treatment, the therapist records the number of positive self statements. The data are as follows:

| | Number of Positive Statements | |
|---|---|---|
| Subject | Before | After |
| A | 4 | 6 |
| B | 3 | 8 |
| C | 5 | 8 |
| D | 2 | 7 |

Is there a significant effect of the treatment? Use the .01 level of significance.

## Answers to Additional Problems

1. A repeated measures design tends to be more precise or more powerful than an independent measures design because it eliminates variability due to individual differences. Also, a repeated-measure design uses fewer subjects than an independent-measures design. However, the results from a repeated-measures experiment can be confounded by carry-over effects.

2. For these data, $\overline{D} = 5.7$, s =12, and t(15) = 1.90. For a one-tailed test the critical value is 1.753. Reject $H_0$ and conclude that there has been a significant change.

3.    The standard error for these data is 4 and $t(24) = 18/4$
      $= 4.50$.   Reject $H_0$ and conclude that the preparatory
      course has a significant effect.

4.    For these data $\overline{D} = -3$, $s = 3$ and $t(8) = -3.00$.   Reject
      $H_0$ and conclude that the relaxation training has a
      significant effect.

5.    For these data, $\overline{D} = 3.75$, $s = 1.5$, and $t(3) = 5.00$.
      Fail to reject $H_0$.   These data are not sufficient to
      conclude that there has been a change with $\alpha = .01$.

# CHAPTER 12
# ESTIMATION

## Multiple-Choice Questions

1. Which of the following would result in a larger width for a confidence interval?
   a. use a larger sample
   b. select a smaller % confidence
   *c. obtaining a sample with large variability
   d. none of the above

2. Which of the following most closely resembles the general form of an interval estimate?
   a. statistic = parameter ± error
   b. statistic = parameter × error
   *c. parameter = statistic ± error
   d. error = parameter ± statistic

3. The purpose of a confidence interval is to
   *a. use a sample mean to estimate the value of a population mean
   b. use $\mu$ to estimate the value of a sample mean
   c. use a level of confidence to estimate a sample mean
   d. use the sample mean to determine a level of confidence

4.  For a single sample of n = 23, the t values used to determine the 90% confidence interval are
    a.  ±1.721
    b.  ±2.819
    c.  ±2.074
    *d. ±1.717

5.  The correct formula for estimating the value of $\mu$ with the z-score is
    a.  $\mu = \bar{X} \pm z\sigma$
    *b. $\mu = \bar{X} \pm z\sigma_{\bar{X}}$
    c.  $\mu = \bar{X} \pm zs_{\bar{X}-\bar{X}}$
    d.  $\mu = \bar{X} \pm zt$

6.  Holding everything else constant, decreasing sample size
    a.  decreases standard error
    b.  increases degrees of freedom
    *c. increases the width of the confidence interval
    d.  all of the above

7.  A sample of n = 16 scores is obtained from a normal distribution with $\sigma = 20$. The sample mean is $\bar{X} = 52$. Using this information, the point estimate of the population mean is
    a.  57
    *b. 52
    c.  52 ± 20
    d.  52 ± 5

8. Assuming a normal distribution, what z-score values would be used for the 70% confidence level?

   *a   +1.04, −1.04

    b.   +0.39, −0.39

    c.   +0.67, −0.67

    d.   insufficient information to determine

9. A sample of n = 25 scores is obtained from a normal population with $\sigma$ = 15.  If the sample mean is $\bar{X}$ = 37, the 95% confidence interval for $\mu$ would be

    a.   37 ± 1.96(15)

    b.   37 ± 0.95(15)

   *c.   37 ± 1.96(3)

    d.   37 ± 0.95(3)

10. The 95% confidence interval for $\mu$ is computed from sample data and the interval estimate ranges from 65 to 75.  This indicates that

    a.   95% of the scores in the population fall between X = 65 and X = 75

    b.   you should reject $H_0$ for any sample value between 65 and 75

    c.   the standard error is 10

   *d.   there is a 95% chance that the population mean falls somewhere between 65 and 75.

11. The correct formula for estimating the value of $\mu_D$ is

   *a.   $\mu_D = \bar{D} \pm ts_{\bar{D}}$

    b.   $\mu_D = s_{\bar{X}} \pm t\bar{D}$

    c.   $\mu_D = \bar{D} \pm ts$

    d.   $\mu_D = \bar{X} \pm ts$

Questions 12 and 13 refer to the following data:

|          | Treatment 1 | Treatment 2 |
|----------|:-----------:|:-----------:|
|          | n = 4       | n = 4       |
|          | $\bar{X}$ = 24 | $\bar{X}$ = 16 |
|          | SS = 38     | SS = 34     |

12. For these data, the t values for the 99% confidence interval are
    a.  ±3.143
    b.  ±2.998
    *c.  ±3.707
    d.  ±2.58

13. The 95% confidence interval for $\mu_1 - \mu_2$ is
    a.  24 ± 1.96(12)
    *b.  8 ± 2.447($\sqrt{6}$)
    c.  8 ± 2.447($\sqrt{12}$)
    d.  8 ± 1.964($\sqrt{6}$)

14. The point estimate for $\mu_1 - \mu_2$ is
    a.  24
    b.  16
    c.  $\sqrt{12}$
    *d.  8

## True-False Questions

F   1.  For confidence intervals, precision increases as the interval gets wider.

F.  2.  Estimation is used to determine whether or not a treatment effect has occurred.

T     3.   If all other factors are held constant, as degrees
      of freedom increase, the width of a confidence interval
      will decrease.

T     4.   When making a point estimate for $\mu$, you should use
      the value of $\bar{X}$.

T     5.   If the 90% confidence interval for $\mu$ is from 34 to
      50, then there is a 10% chance that $\mu$ does not fall
      within that range.

F     6.   For an 75% confidence interval, the correct
      z-score values are z = +0.75 and z = -0.75.

F     7.   When estimating the value for $\mu_D$, you should use $\sigma_{\bar{x}}$
      for the standard error.

T     8.   When estimating the value for the difference
      between two population means, you should use $s_{\bar{x}-\bar{x}}$ for
      the standard error.

F     9.   Holding everything else constant, the width of the
      confidence interval will increase as the standard error
      decreases.

F     10. A researcher computes a 95% confidence interval for
      $\mu$ based on a sample of n = 25 scores.  If another
      sample of 25 scores is selected, there is a 95%
      probability that the new sample mean will be contained
      within the researcher's interval.

T     11. Sample 1 has n = 6 and sample 2 has n = 8.  The t
      values for the 95% confidence interval are ±2.179.

T    12. The correct formula for estimating the population
     mean, when σ is not known, is $\mu = \bar{X} \pm ts_{\bar{x}}$.


                    Additional Questions and Problems


1.   Describe point estimates and interval estimates in
     terms of their confidence and precision in estimating
     $\mu$.


2.   A random sample of n = 25 scores is obtained from a
     population that has  σ = 5.  The mean for the sample is
     $\bar{X}$ = 34.4.
     a.    Use these data to make a point estimate of the
           population mean.
     b.    Make an interval estimate of $\mu$ so that you are 90%
           confident that the true population mean is in
           your interval.


3.   A sample of freshmen take a reading comprehension test.
     For the following sample data, determine the boundaries
     of the 99% confidence interval for $\mu$.

          18    13    12    15    12


4.   For a sample of n = 9, $\bar{X}$ = 72 with SS = 800.  Make a
     point estimate of $\mu$ and determine the 90% confidence
     interval for $\mu$.


5.   For a sample of n = 25 high school students, the mean
     improvement in SAT scores following a preparatory
     course was $\bar{D}$ = 44 points with s = 36.  On average, how
     much improvement can be expected for the population of
     high school students?  Use a 90% confidence interval.

6.  A researcher would like to estimate how much difference in cigarette smoking results from viewing graphic videos (including an autopsy) on the harmful effects of smoking. A sample of n = 8 smokers view the video and the number of packs of cigarettes each person smoked during the following week is recorded. A second sample of n = 8 smokers serves as a control group and does not view the video. The data are as follows:

|  Controls | Video Viewers |
|---|---|
| $\overline{X}$ = 17.5 | $\overline{X}$ = 8.1 |
| SS = 122 | SS = 102 |

a.  Use the sample data to make a point estimate of the mean difference in smoking behavior between the control group and video viewers.

b.  Make an interval estimate of the mean difference so that you are 80% confident that the population mean difference is in your interval.

Answers to Additional Problems

1.  Point estimates are perfectly precise but have no confidence. Interval estimates provide confidence (the wider the interval, the more confidence), but they give up precision (the wider the interval, the less precision).

2.  a.  Use $\overline{X}$ = 34.4 for the point estimate of $\mu$.
    b.  $\mu$ = 34.4 ± (1.65)(1). The confidence interval extends from 32.75 to 36.05.

3. $\mu = 14 \pm 4.604(1.14)$, df = 4. The confidence interval extends from 8.75 to 19.25.

4. For the point estimate, use $\bar{X} = 72$. $\mu = 72 \pm 1.86(3.33)$, df = 8. The confidence interval extends from 65.81 to 78.19.

5. $\mu = 44 \pm 1.711(7.2)$, df = 24. The confidence interval extends from 31.68 to 56.32.

6. a. Use $\mu_1 - \mu_2 = 9.4$ for the point estimate.
   b. $\mu_1 - \mu_2 = 9.4 \pm 1.345(2)$, df = 14. The confidence interval extends from 6.71 to 12.09.

# CHAPTER 13

# INTRODUCTION TO

# ANALYSIS OF VARIANCE

## Multiple-Choice Questions

1.  For an experiment comparing more than two treatment
    conditions you should use analysis of variance rather
    than separate t tests because
    a.  you are less likely to make a mistake in the
        computations of ANOVA
    b.  a test based on variances is more sensitive than a
        test based on means
    *c.  ANOVA has less risk of a Type I Error
    d.  ANOVA has less risk of a Type II Error

2.  The distinction between the "testwise" alpha level and
    the "experimentwise" alpha level is important
    a.  whenever you do an analysis of variance
    b.  only when the study is comparing exactly two
        treatments
    *c.  only when the study is comparing more than two
        treatments
    d.  only when there are fewer than 30 scores in each
        treatment

3.  When the null hypothesis is true for an ANOVA, the expected value for the F-ratio is
    a.  zero
    *b. 1.00
    c.  k - 1
    d.  N - k

4.  In analysis of variance, the F-ratio is a ratio of
    a.  two (or more) sample means
    *b. two variances
    c.  sample means divided by sample variances
    d.  none of the above

5.  For an independent-measures experiment comparing three treatment conditions with a sample of $n = 10$ in each treatment, the F-ratio would have degrees of freedom equal to
    a.  29
    b.  2, 29
    *c. 2, 27
    d.  3, 27

6.  The value for the within-treatments degrees of freedom, $df_{within}$, is determined by
    a.  n - 1
    b.  N - 1
    c.  k - 1
    *d. N - k

7.  For an F-ratio with df = 2,10, the critical value for a hypothesis test using $\alpha = .05$ would be
    *a. 4.10
    b.  7.56
    c.  19.39
    d.  99.40

8. A researcher reports an F-ratio with df = 3,20 for an independent-measures experiment. How many treatment conditions were compared in this experiment?

    a. 3
   *b. 4
    c. 21
    d. 24

9. A researcher reports an F-ratio with df = 3,20 for an independent-measures experiment. How many individual subjects participated in the experiment?

    a. 3
    b. 4
    c. 21
   *d. 24

10. An experiment compares two treatment conditions with a sample of n = 20 in each treatment. If the data are analyzed with ANOVA, the analysis would have $df_{total}$ = _____ .

    a. 18
    b. 19
    c. 38
   *d. 39

11. In analysis of variance, the term "factor" refers to

    a. a dependent variable
   *b. an independent variable
    c. a treatment mean
    d. a treatment total

12. A "treatment effect" refers to differences between scores that are caused by the different treatment conditions. The differences (or variability) produced by "treatment effects" will contribute
    *a. to the numerator of the F-ratio
    b. to the denominator of the F-ratio
    c. to both the numerator and the denominator of the F-ratio
    d. "treatment effects" are removed before the F-ratio is computed

13. Post hoc tests are necessary after an ANOVA whenever
    a. Ho is rejected
    b. there are more than two treatments
    *c. a and b
    d. you always should do post hoc tests after an ANOVA

14. The purpose of post hoc test is to
    *a. determine which treatments are different
    b. determine how much difference there is between treatments
    c. determine whether or not a Type I Error was made in the ANOVA
    d. determine whether or not a complete ANOVA is justified

15. In general the distribution of F-ratios is
    a. symmetrical with a mean of zero
    *b. positively skewed with all values greater than or equal to zero
    c. negatively skewed with all values greater than or equal to zero
    d. symmetrical with a mean equal to $df_{between}$

16.  In analysis of variance MS provides a measure of
    *a.   variance
     b.   average differences among means
     c.   the total variability for the set of N scores
     d.   the overall mean for the set of N scores

17.  $SS_{between\ treatments}$ measures
    *a.   differences between the treatment means
     b.   differences between subjects inside the treatments
     c.   the sum of the scores for each of the treatments
     d.   the sum of the treatment totals

18.  In an independent–measures experiment with three
     treatment conditions, each treatment has the same mean,
     $\bar{X}$ = 5.5.  For these data $SS_{between\ treatments}$ equals
    *a.   0
     b.   1.00
     c.   3(5.50)
     d.   cannot be determined from the information given

19.  An analysis of variance comparing two treatments
     produced an F-ratio of F = 4.00.  If the same data had
     been evaluated using a t test, the t statistic would be
     equal to
    *a.   2
     b.   4
     c.   8
     d.   16

Questions 20 through 22 refer to the following set of data

| Treatment 1 | Treatment 2 | Treatment 3 |
|---|---|---|
| n = 5 | n = 5 | n = 5 |
| T = 5 | T = 10 | T = 15 |
| SS = 25 | SS = 20 | SS = 15 |

20. In the analysis of variance for these data, $SS_{within}$ is equal to

    a.  10

    b.  15

  *c.  60

    d.  cannot be determined from the information given

21. In the analysis of variance for these data, the between-treatments degrees of freedom is equal to

  *a.   2

    b.   3

    c.  12

    d.  14

22. In the analysis of variance for these data, $SS_{between\ treatments}$ is equal to

    a.  5

  *b.  10

    c.  15

    d.  60

## True-False Questions

T    1.  The basic "analysis" in ANOVA involves partitioning the total variability into two components: between-treatments variability and within-treatments variability.

F    2.  Analysis of variance is used to test for differences in variance between two or more populations.

F    3.   When the null hypothesis is true, the F-ratio for analysis of variance is expected to be zero.

F    4.   With k = 3 treatments, the alternative hypothesis for analysis of variance always states that all three treatment means are different.

F    5.   With k = 3 treatments, rejecting the null hypothesis for analysis of variance means you have concluded that all three treatment means are different.

T    6.   When the null hypothesis is true, the F-ratio is <u>balanced</u> so that the numerator and the denominator are both measuring exactly the same sources of variance.

F    7.   As variability (differences) increases inside each treatment condition, the value of the F-ratio will also increase.

T    8.   The larger the differences (variability) between treatment means, the larger the F-ratio.

T    9.   The critical region for the F-ratio from an analysis of variance is located entirely in one tail of the distribution.

F    10.   The F-distribution table lists a critical value of F = 4.26 for an F-ratio with df = 2,9 and $\alpha$ = .05.   If the data produce an F-ratio of F(2,9) = 4.10, the correct decision would be "reject $H_0$ at the .05 level of significance."

F    11.   For an experiment with k = 3 treatments,   $MS_{between}$ = 10.   For this analysis, $SS_{between}$ = 30.

T     12.   Post tests would <u>not</u> be needed if $H_0$ were rejected in an ANOVA comparing k = 2 treatments.

F     13.   Post tests are used after analysis of variance to determine why the null hypothesis was not rejected.

F     14.   Post hoc tests are used to reduce the risk of a Type I error.

T     15.   The distribution of F-ratios is positively skewed.

T     16.   It is impossible to obtain a negative value for an F-ratio.

T     17.   In analysis of variance, a value of F = 0 indicates that all of the samples have exactly the same mean.

T     18.   An F-ratio of F = 1.00 indicates that the data provide no evidence of any treatment effect.

T     19.   An ANOVA with k = 2 treatments produced an F-ratio of 1.00.  If the data were analyzed with an independent measures t statistic, the value of t would also be 1.00.

T     20.   An independent-measures t test comparing two treatments has df = 20.  If the same data were analyzed using ANOVA the F-ratio would have df =  1, 20.

# Additional Questions and Problems

1. What value is expected, on average, for the F-ratio in ANOVA when the null hypothesis is true? Explain why this value is expected.

2. Describe the circumstances where you must use ANOVA instead of t tests, and explain why t tests are inappropriate in these circumstances.

3. State the alternative hypothesis ($H_0$) for an ANOVA comparing four treatment conditions. Explain why the hypothesis is stated in this way.

4. A psychologist would like to examine the effects of a new drug on the activity level of animals. Three samples of rats are selected with n = 5 in each sample. The rats in the fist sample serve as a control and do not get any of the drug. The rats in the second group receive 1 milligram (mg) each and the rats in the third group get 5 mg each. The psychologist records the activity level for each animal. The data from this experiment are presented below. Do these data indicate any significant differences among the three groups? Test with $\alpha = .05$.

| no drug | 1 mg | 5 mg | |
|---------|------|------|---|
| 0 | 2 | 5 | |
| 2 | 2 | 3 | |
| 2 | 3 | 2 | G = 30 |
| 0 | 2 | 2 | $\Sigma X^2 = 82$ |
| 1 | 1 | 3 | |
| T = 5 | T = 10 | T = 15 | |
| SS = 4 | SS = 2 | SS = 6 | |

5.  A psychologist would like to know whether the change in seasons has any consistent effect on people's mood. In the middle of each of the four seasons the psychologist selects a random sample of n = 25 students. Each individual in these four separate samples is given a standardized mood/depression questionnaire. The data from this study were examined using an analysis of variance and the results are shown in the summary table below. Fill in all missing values in the table.

| Source | SS | df | MS | |
|---|---|---|---|---|
| Between Treatments | ____ | ____ | 50 | F = ____ |
| Within Treatments | 960 | ____ | ____ | |
| Total | ____ | ____ | | |

6.  The data below are from an independent—measures experiment comparing three difference treatment conditions. The summary table shows the results of the analysis of variance for these data. Use the Scheffe test to determine which of the three treatments are significantly different from each other. Use the .05 level of significance for all tests.

| Treatment 1 | Treatment 2 | Treatment 3 |
|---|---|---|
| 0 | 1 | 5 |
| 0 | 4 | 2 |
| 0 | 1 | 6 |
| 2 | 0 | 3 |

| Source | SS | df | MS | |
|---|---|---|---|---|
| Between | 26 | 2 | 13 | F = 6.50 |
| Within | 18 | 9 | 2 | |
| Total | 44 | 11 | | |

# Answers to Additional Problems

1. When the null hypothesis is true, the F-ratio is expected to be near 1.00. The structure of the F-ratio is balanced so that the numerator and denominator are measuring identical sources of variance if the treatment effect is zero ($H_0$ is true).

2. ANOVA must be used when there are more than two treatment conditions. In this situation it would require several t tests to compare all the treatments, and the more tests that are done the more risk there is for a Type I error.

3. With k = 4 treatments the alternative hypothesis would simply state, "At least one mean is different from the others." This general statement is used because there are several different alternatives to $H_0$ and it usually is not productive to try to list them all.

4.

| Source | SS | df | MS | |
|--------|-----|-----|-----|-----|
| Between Treatments | 10 | 2 | 5 | $F(2,12) = 5$ |
| Within Treatments | 12 | 12 | 1 | |
| Total | 22 | 14 | | |

Reject $H_0$ at the .05 level of significance.

5.

| Source | SS | df | MS | |
|--------|------|-----|-----|-----|
| Between Treatments | 150 | 3 | 50 | $F = 5.00$ |
| Within Treatments | 960 | 96 | 10 | |
| Total | 1110 | 99 | | |

6.  Starting with the largest mean difference:
    Treatment 1 versus 3:
    $MS_{between} = 12.25$, $F(2,9) = 6.125$ (significant)
    Treatment 2 versus 3:
    $MS_{between} = 6.25$, $F(2,9) = 3.125$ (not significant)
    No other treatment differences are significant.

# CHAPTER 14
# CORRELATION AND
# REGRESSION

## Multiple-Choice Questions

1.  The computation formula for sum of products is
    a.  $\Sigma XY^2 - \dfrac{\Sigma X \Sigma Y}{n-1}$       c.  $\Sigma(X - \bar{X})^2 \Sigma(Y - \bar{Y})^2$

    b.  $\Sigma(X - \bar{X})(Y - \bar{Y})$      *d.  $\Sigma XY - \dfrac{\Sigma X \Sigma Y}{n}$

2.  Which of the following sets of correlations correctly shows the highest to lowest degree of relationship?
    *a.  -0.91, +0.83, +0.10, -0.03
    b.  -0.91, +0.83, -0.03, -0.10
    c.  +0.83, +0.10, -0.91, -0.03
    d.  +0.83, +0.10, -0.03, -0.91

3.  Suppose the correlation between height and weight for adults is +0.80.  What proportion (or percent) of the variability in weight is due to the relationship with height?
    a.  80%
    *b.  64%
    c.  100 - 80 = 20%
    d.  40%

Questions 4 and 5 concern the following data:

| X | Y |
|---|---|
| 2 | 4 |
| 5 | 2 |
| 3 | 5 |
| 2 | 5 |

4.  For these data, SP equals

    a.  6

  *b.  -5

    c.  36

    d.  none of the above

5.  For these data, the Pearson correlation

    a.  is positive

  *b.  is negative

    c.  is zero

    d.  cannot be determined  with information provided

6.  In the general linear equation, $Y = bX + a$, the value of a is called

    a.  the slope constant

  *b.  the Y-intercept

    c.  the X-intercept

    d.  the beta factor

7.  In the linear equation $Y = 3X + 1$, when X increases by 4 points, Y will increase by

    a.  4 points

    b.  7 points

  *c.  12 points

    d.  13 points

8. In the general linear equation, Y = bX + a, the value of b is called the
   a. X intercept
   b. Y intercept
   c. correlation between X and Y
   *d. slope

9. What information is <u>cannot</u> be determined from the general linear equation, Y = bX + a?
   *a. the correlation between X and Y
   b. the slope
   c. the Y intercept
   d. a and c

10. The regression equation is determined by minimizing
    a. the total error between the X and Y values
    b. the total error between the predicted Y values and the actual Y values
    c. the total squared error between the X and the Y values
    *d. the total squared error between the predicted Y values and the actual Y values

11. Which of the following points is on the line defined by the equation Y = 4X + 2
    a. X = 1 and Y = 4
    *b. X = 0.5 and Y = 4
    c. X = 2 and Y = 8
    d. X = 3 and Y = 9

12. The entrance fee for a theme park is $20. Tickets for each ride and attraction are $3 apiece. Which of the following equations describes the relation between the total cost (Y) and the number of tickets purchased (X) in a single visit to the park?
    a.  $Y = 20X + 3$
    b.  $Y = 60X$
    *c.  $Y = 3X + 20$
    d.  $X = 3Y + 20$

13. A set of X and Y scores has $\bar{X} = 4$, $SS_x = 15$, $\bar{Y} = 5$, $SP = 30$. What is the regression equation for predicting Y from X?
    a.  $\hat{Y} = 3X + 2$
    b.  $\hat{Y} = 2X + 3$
    c.  $\hat{Y} = 10X + 13$
    *d.  $\hat{Y} = 2X - 3$

14. If there is a negative correlation between X and Y then the regression equation, $\hat{Y} = bX + a$ will have
    a.  $b > 0$
    *b.  $b < 0$
    c.  $a > 0$
    d.  $a < 0$

## True-False Questions

T    1.  If decreases in the X variable are accompanied by decreases in the Y variable, then the correlation between X and Y is positive.

F    2.  If the value of the Pearson correlation is $r = 0$, then all data points on a scatterplot would fall on a straight line with a Y intercept of zero.

T    3.   Anytime the sum of products, SP, has a value less than zero, the correlation also must be negative.

F    4.   Suppose it was observed that there is a correlation of $r = -0.81$ between a driver's age and the cost of the car insurance. This correlation would mean that, in general, the older people pay more for car insurance.

T    5.   A researcher obtained a correlation of $r = +0.62$ between the amount of time spent watching television and level of blood cholesterol.  This means that there is a general tendency for people who watch less television also to have lower blood cholesterol.

F    6.   Suppose there is a correlation of $+0.87$ between the length of time a person is in prison and the amount of aggression the person displays on a psychological inventory.  This means that spending a longer amount of time in prison causes people to become more aggressive.

T    7.   It is possible for two sets of data have the same regression equation, but different correlations.

F    8.   If two sets of data have the same correlation (for example, $r = +0.80$), they also must have the same regression equation.

T    9.   It is possible for the regression equation to have none of the actual (observed) data points located on the regression line.

T    10.   The point defined by $X = 2$ and $Y = 5$ is located on the line defined by the equation $Y = 4X - 3$.

F   11.   A correlation of r = +0.68 will result in more
accurate predictions than a situation where r = -0.95.

F   12.   If the Y intercept is positive, then the
regression equation will have a positive slope.

T   13.   When testing a hypothesis about a correlation, the
null hypothesis states that the population correlation
is zero.

### Additional Questions and Problems

1.   Describe what is meant by a "negative relationship"
between two variables.

2.   For the data below, compute the Pearson correlation.

| X | Y |
|---|---|
| 3 | 4 |
| 2 | 5 |
| 1 | 9 |
| 6 | 2 |

3.   For the data below, compute the Pearson correlation and
find the regression equation for predicting Y from X.

| X | Y |
|---|---|
| 1 | 2 |
| 2 | 3 |
| 4 | 2 |
| 5 | 6 |
| 8 | 7 |

4.  Find the regression equation for predicting Y from X
    for the following set of scores.

    | X | Y |
    |---|----|
    | 0 | 9 |
    | 1 | 7 |
    | 2 | 11 |

5.  A sample of n = 20 pairs of scores (X and Y values)
    produces a correlation of r = -0.46.  Are these sample
    data sufficient to conclude that there is a nonzero
    correlation between X and Y in the population?  Test at
    the .05 level of significance.

## Answers to Additional Problems

1.  In a negative relationship there is a tendency for one
    variable to decrease as the other variable increases.
    The two variables tend to move in opposite directions.

2.  $SS_x = 14$, $SS_y = 26$, $SP = -17$, $r = -0.89$.

3.  $SS_x = 30$, $SS_y = 22$, $SP = 22$, $r = +0.86$,
    $\hat{Y} = 0.73X + 1.08$.

4.  $SS_x = 2$, $SP = 2$, $\bar{X} = 1$, and $\bar{Y} = 9$.  $\hat{Y} = (1)X + 8$.

5.  $H_0: \rho = 0$.  For these data, df = 18 and the critical
    value for r from Table B.5 is 0.444.  $H_0$ is rejected, p
    < .05.

# CHAPTER 15
# THE CHI-SQUARE STATISTIC: TESTS FOR GOODNESS OF FIT AND INDEPENDENCE

## Multiple-Choice Questions

1.  A characteristic of nonparametric tests is that
    a.  they require a numerical score for each individual
    b.  they require assumptions about the population distribution(s)
    c.  they evaluate hypothesis about population means or variances
    *d.  none of the above

2.  The term "observed frequency" refers to
    *a.  the frequencies found in the sample data
    b.  the frequencies found in the population being examined
    c.  ideal frequencies that are assumed to exist for the population being examined
    d.  the frequencies computed from the null hypothesis

3. In the test for goodness of fit, the chi-square statistic has degrees of freedom equal to
   a. n - 1
   b. n - 2
   c. n - C (where C is the number of categories)
   *d. none of the above

4. The chi-square test for goodness-of-fit evaluates
   a. the relationship between two variables
   b. the mean differences between two or more treatments
   *c. the shape or proportions for a population distribution
   d. none of the above

5. In a chi-square test for independence or goodness of fit
   a. $\Sigma f_e = n$
   b. $\Sigma f_e = \Sigma f_o$
   *c. a and b
   d. none of the above

6. The null hypothesis for the chi-square test for goodness of fit specifies
   a. proportions for a sample distribution
   *b. proportions for a population distribution
   c. frequencies for a sample distribution
   d. frequencies for a population distribution

7. The chi-square distribution is
   a. symmetrical with a mean of zero
   *b. positively skewed with all values greater than or equal to zero
   c. negatively skewed with all values greater than or equal to zero
   d. symmetrical with a mean equal to n - 1

8. A researcher is using a chi-square test to determine whether there are any preferences among four brands of cola. With $\alpha$ = .05 and a sample of n = 30, the critical region for the hypothesis test would have a boundary of
   *a. 7.81
   b. 9.49
   c. 42.56
   d. 43.77

9. For a fixed level of significance, the critical value for chi-square will
   a. increase as n increases
   b. decrease as n increases
   *c. increase as df increases
   d. decrease as df increases

10. As the differences between $f_e$ and $f_o$ increase
    *a. the likelihood of rejecting $H_0$ also increases
    b. the likelihood of rejecting $H_0$ decreases
    c. the critical value for chi-square increases
    d. the critical value for chi-square decreases

11. The chi-square test for independence is used to test for
    a.  a mean difference between two populations
    b.  a difference between a sample distribution and a population distribution
    c.  a difference in variance between two populations
    *d. a relationship between two variables

12. The chi-square test for independence can be used to evaluate
    a.  the relationship between two variables
    b.  differences between two or more population frequency distributiions
    *c. all of the above
    d.  none of the above

13. A researcher is using a chi-square test to determine whether people have any preferences among three brands of color televisions.  The null hypothesis for this test would state
    a.  there are real preferences in the population
    b.  one-third of the sample will prefer each brand
    *c. one-third of the population prefers each brand
    d.  in the population, one brand will be preferred over the other two

14. The chi-square test for independence has degrees of freedom given by
    a.  R x C
    b.  R x C(n - 1)
    c.  n - R x C
    *d. (R - 1)(C - 1)

15. A basic assumption for a chi-square hypothesis test is
    a.  the population distribution(s) must be normal
    b.  the scores must come from an interval or ratio scale
    *c. the observations must be independent
    d.  all of the above

16. The chi-square statistic should not be used if
    a.  $f_e > 5$ for any cell
    *b. $f_e < 5$ for any cell
    c.  $f_e = f_o$ for any cell
    d.  none of the above

    Questions 17 and 18 refer to the following frequency data obtained from a sample of n = 100 adults.

|                    | Males | Females |
|--------------------|-------|---------|
| Registered Voter   | 50    | 25      |
| Not Registered     | 10    | 15      |

17. For a chi-square test for independence, the expected frequency for registered males would
    a.  15
    b.  25
    *c. 45
    d.  50

18. The chi-square statistic in a test for independence would have degrees of freedom equal to
    *a. 1
    b.  3
    c.  96
    d.  99

F     1.    The "observed frequencies" for a chi-square test
            represent an ideal, hypothetical distribution that
            would be obtained if the sample were in perfect
            agreement with the null hypothesis.

F.    2.    The data for a chi-square test are called
            "expected frequencies."

T     3.    In a chi-square test, the observed frequencies are
            always whole numbers.

T     4.    The chi-square test for independence requires that
            each observation be categorized on two separate
            variables.

F     5.    In the chi-square test for independence, a
            positive value for the chi-square statistic
            indicates a positive correlation between the two
            variables.

F     6.    In the chi-square test for goodness of fit the
            null hypothesis always predicts equal frequencies
            for all categories.

F     7.    In general, a large value for the chi-square
            statistic indicates that the null hypothesis is
            correct.

T     8.    The value of df for a chi-square tests does not
            depend on the sample size (n).

T    9.    The chi-square test for independence is similar to a correlation in that is evaluates the relationship between two variables.

T    10.   The chi-square test for independence is similar to an independent-measures t test in that it can be used to evaluate the difference between two populations or two treatment conditions.

T    11.   For a fixed level of significance, the critical value for chi-square increases as the degrees of freedom increase.

T    12.   It is impossible to obtain a value less than zero for the chi-square statistic, unless a mistake is made.

F    13.   In a chi-square test for independence, the expected frequencies in one row of the matrix are identical to the expected frequencies in any other row.

F    14.   It is impossible for a chi-square test for independence to have df = 1.

F    15.   A researcher is using a chi-square test for goodness of fit to determine whether there is any preference between two brands of chocolate-chip cookies. With $\alpha$ = .05 and a sample of n = 25, the critical value for the chi-square statistic would be 36.42.

T    16.   A chi-square test should not be used if any expected frequency is less than five.

F.    17.    For a chi-square test for independence it is possible for one individual to be counted in two different cells provided the two cells are not in the same row or in the same column.


## Additional Questions and Problems

1.    Explain how the chi-square tests differ from parametric tests (such as t tests or ANOVA) with respect to
   a.    The hypotheses
   b.    The data
   c.    The assumptions underlying the test

2.    A researcher would like to determine whether people have any preferences among three national brands of instant coffee. A sample of thirty people is obtained and each person tastes all three brands, then identifies his/her preference. The resulting frequency data are presented below. On the basis of these data can the researcher conclude that there are significant preferences in the general population? Test at the .05 level of significance.

| Brand A | Brand B | Brand C |
|---------|---------|---------|
| 5       | 14      | 11      |

   a.    State the hypotheses.
   b.    Locate the critical region.
   c.    Compute the chi-square statistic.
   d.    What decision should the researcher make?

3. A survey in 1980 showed that 50% of the population approved of smoking in public places, 30% disapproved, and 20% had no opinion. A sample of n = 60 people obtained this year produced the frequency distribution shown below. On the basis of these data, can you conclude that there has been a significant change in attitudes toward public smoking? Test at the .05 level of significance.

| Approve | Disapprove | No Opinion |
|---------|------------|------------|
| 20 | 30 | 10 |

   a. State the hypotheses.
   b. Locate the critical region.
   c. Compute the chi-square statistic.
   d. What decision should be made?

4. A proposed city ordinance would completely prohibit skateboarding on all city streets and sidewalks. A researcher would like to examine people's attitudes toward this proposed ban, with a specific interest in the relation between attitude and age. A random sample of n = 100 people is obtained and the researcher classifies each individual according to age and his/her attitude. The frequency data are presented below. Do these data indicate any relationship between age and attitude? Test at the .05 level of significance.

|  | For | Against | No Opinion |
|---|-----|---------|------------|
| under 30 | 26 | 33 | 16 |
| over 30 | 14 | 7 | 4 |

AGE

   a. State the hypotheses.

b.   Locate the critical region.

c.   Compute the chi-square statistic.

d.   What decision should be made?


## Answers to Additional Problems

1.   As nonparametric tests, the chi-square tests state
     general hypotheses about the entire population without
     any reference to a specific population parameter.  The
     data for a chi-square test consist of frequencies, but
     the data for a t test or ANOVA consist of scores that
     can be added, multiplied, squared, etc.  Finally, the
     chi-square tests do not require any assumptions about
     population parameters.  The t tests and ANOVA require
     normal populations and homogeneity of variance for
     tests with independent-measures designs.

2.   a.   The three brands are equally preferred in the
          population.

     b.   With df = 2, the critical region consists of
          chi-square values greater than 5.99.

     c.   The expected frequencies are: 10, 10, and 10.  The
          chi-square statistic is 4.20.

     d.   Fail to reject $H_0$.

3.   a.   The null hypothesis states that there has been no
          change in the population opinions.  The
          percentages should still be 50% approve, 30%
          disapprove, and 20% no opinion.

     b.   With df = 2, the critical region consists of
          chi-square values greater than 5.99

     c.   The expected frequencies are: 30, 18, and 12.  The
          chi-square statistic is 11.66.

     d.   Reject $H_0$.

4.  a.  The null hypothesis states that in the population an individual's attitude toward the skateboarding ban is independent of age.

    b.  With df = 2, the critical region consists of chi-square values greater than 5.99.

    c.  The expected frequencies are:

|          | for | against | no opinion |
|----------|-----|---------|------------|
| under 30 | 30  | 30      | 15         |
| over 30  | 10  | 10      | 5          |

    For these data the chi-square statistic is 3.60.

    d.  Fail to reject $H_0$.

# CHAPTER 16
# INTRODUCTION TO MINITAB

## Multiple-Choice Questions

1.  Minitab commands have two parts, known as
    a.  columns and rows
    b.  constants and rows
    *c. command names and arguments
    d.  prompts and columns

2.  You can get assistance from Minitab by typing the
    following command:
    a.  ASSIST
    *b. HELP
    c.  COMMAND
    d.  STOP

3.  Simultaneously entering data into several columns is
    accomplished by the following command:
    *a. READ
    b.  ENTER
    c.  SET
    d.  all of the above

4.  The command END tells the computer
    a.  you have completed the Minitab session
    b.  to stop printing additional data
    c.  to clear the screen
    *d. you have finished entering data

5.    If you want to work with a saved worksheet, which of
      the following commands will give you access to it?
      a.    PRINT
      b.    GET
   *c.    RETRIEVE
      d.    LOAD

6.    Two variables have been named SCORE and PRACTICE.  How
      would you instruct Minitab to construct a scatterplot
      with SCORE on the Y-axis?
   *a.    PLOT 'SCORE' 'PRACTICE'
      b.    PLOT 'PRACTICE' 'SCORE'
      c.    DOTPLOT 'SCORE' 'PRACTICE'
      d.    GRAPH 'PRACTICE' 'SCORE'

7.    The command TWOSAMPLE performs the following:
      a.    an analysis of variance for the two samples
      b.    a correlation between the two samples
      c.    combining the data of two samples into one column
   *d.    an independent-measures t test

8.    You can activate a printer to receive output by typing
      a.    PRINT
   *b.    PAPER
      c.    NEWPAGE
      d.    ACTIVATE

9.    The command TTEST is used for
      a.    an independent-measures t test
      b.    a single-sample t test
   *c.    a single-sample or repeated-measures t test
      d.    any type of t test

10. If you wanted to get means and standard deviations with a single command, you could type
   *a. DESCRIBE
    b. STATISTICS
    c. SUMMARY
    d. INFO


## True-False Questions

F   1.   The Minitab worksheet contains columns, rows, and commands.

T   2.   The argument for a command consists of column numbers, constants, column names, or a file name.

F   3.   If you wish to use a subcommand, then the command must be followed by a slash (/).

F   4.   You can get help during a Minitab session by striking the escape (Esc) key.

F   5.   The command SET allows you to enter data into several columns at once.

T   6.   The PRINT command will let you view data you have just entered.

T   7.   SAVE is used to store a Minitab worksheet.

F   8.   Basic descriptive statistics can be obtained by using the command INFO.

T    9.   ONEWAY instructs the computer to perform an
          analysis of variance.

F    10.  CHISQUARE performs the test for goodness of fit.


## Additional Questions and Problems

1.   Identify the function performed by each of the
     following commands:
     a.   LET C4(5) = 12.3
     b.   NAME C1='AGE' C2='INCOME' C3='EDUC'
     c.   DESC 'AGE' 'INCOME' 'EDUC'
     d.   REGRESS 'INCOME' 1 'EDUC'
     e.   PLOT 'INCOME' 'AGE'
     f.   HELP HISTOGRAM
     g.   SAVE 'DEMO'

2.   What is the difference between SET and READ?

3.   What is the distinction between TWOSAMPLE and TTEST?

4.   Identify the following Minitab prompts.
     a.   MTB>
     b.   DATA>
     c.   SUBC>

5.   What is the distinction between END and STOP?

6.   What is provided by the command INFO?

7. Explain the difference between ONEWAY and AOVONEWAY?

8. How may you abbreviate a Minitab command?


Answers to Additional Problems

1. a. The LET command is used to change or correct a score in the worksheet. Here the computer is instructed that the score in the 5th row of column 4 should equal 12.3.

   b. NAME assigns names to variables. In this case, column 1 is called AGE, column 2 is INCOME, and column 3 is named EDUC. (Note that the equal signs in the command are not required.)

   c. DESC is the abbreviated form of DESCRIBE. Descriptive statistics are requested for variables named AGE, INCOME, and EDUC.

   d. REGRESS asks for regression to be performed for the Y variable named INCOME on 1 predictor variable (X) named EDUC.

   e. PLOT requests a scatterplot for variables named INCOME and AGE. INCOME will appear on the Y-axis and AGE on the X-axis.

   f. In this case, the operator uses HELP to get assistance in using HISTOGRAM.

   g. The worksheet is saved in a file named DEMO.

2. With SET, data are entered one column at a time. SET must be used for each column of data to be entered. Alternatively, READ allows several columns of data to be entered at once.

3. TWOSAMPLE is used for an independent-measures t test. TTEST is used for the single-sample t test, or for a repeated-measures t test.

4. a. MTB> is the prompt that indicates Minitab is ready to accept commands. You type your commands after each MTB> prompt.

   b. DATA> indicates that Minitab is ready to accept data entry. You enter your data after each DATA> prompt and then type END when data entry is completed.

   c. SUBC> indicates that Minitab will accept a subcommand. To produce this prompt, type a semi-colon (;) after a Minitab command.

5. END is used after the DATA> prompt when you have finished entering data. STOP is used after the MTB> prompt when you have completed your Minitab session.

6. INFO checks the status of the worksheet. It shows the number (N) of scores and names for each column, and any constants you have assigned.

7.  Both commands perform an analysis of variance (ANOVA).
    However, AOVONEWAY requires a separate column of data
    for each sample in the study.  For ONEWAY, all of the
    data from all of the samples are set in one column.  A
    second column provides group identifiers.

8.  You may abbreviate a Minitab command by using its first
    four letters.

# SECTION II
# SOLUTIONS FOR PROBLEMS
# IN THE TEXT

**NOTE:** Many of the problems in the text require several stages of computation. At each stage there is an opportunity for rounding answers. Depending on the exact sequence of operations used to solve a problem, different individuals will round their answers at different times and in different ways. As a result, you or your students may obtain answers that are slightly different from those presented here. As long as these differences are small, they probably can be attributed to rounding error and should not be a matter for concern.

# CHAPTER 1: INTRODUCTION TO STATISTICS

1.  Descriptive statistics simplify and summarize data. Inferential statistics use sample data to make general conclusions about populations.

2.  The experimental method attempts to establish a cause-and-effect relationship. The correlational method simply determines whether or not a relationship exists.

3.  In the experimental method the experimenter manipulates and controls the independent variable to determine whether or not it has any effect on the dependent variable.

4.  Independent variable is type of diet, dependent variable is cholesterol level.

5.  The independent variable is the type of pill (sleeping drug or placebo).  The dependent variable is the time needed to fall asleep.

6.   a.  brand of cereal preferred
     b.  discrete
     c.  nominal

7.  The independent variable is interrupted versus uninterrupted sleep.  The dependent variable is the number of errors.

8.  Sex and occupation are both nominal.  Age and income are ratio.

9.    a.    discrete

      b.    ratio scale (zero indicates no absences)


10. A nominal scale simply names the categories of
measurement.  An ordinal scale names and orders the
categories.  Order of finish is an ordinal measurement. Sex
of jockeys is a nominal measurement.


11. A discrete variable consists of separate, indivisible
categories.  A continuous variable is divisible into an
infinite number of fractional parts.


12.    a.    You would know which individual had the higher
       score and which had the lower score.
       b.    You would know how much difference there is between
       the two individuals' scores.
       c.    You could compute a ratio for the two measurements
       and make a ratio comparison of the two individuals.
       (For example, you might find that one individual's
       score is 3 times greater than the other.)


13. A construct is a hypothetical concept.  An operational
definition defines a construct in terms of a measurement
procedure.


14.    a.    Add 1 to each score then sum the resulting values.
       b.    Square each score then sum the squared values.
       c.    Subtract 1 from each score and square the resulting
       values.  Then sum the squared values.


15.    a.    $\Sigma X^2 = 51$
       b.    $(\Sigma X)^2 = (13)^2 = 169$
       c.    $\Sigma X + 3 = 16$
       d.    $\Sigma(X + 3) = 25$

16. a. $\Sigma X = 8$
    b. $\Sigma Y = 11$
    c. $\Sigma XY = 34$

17. a. $\Sigma(X + 5) = 70$
    b. $\Sigma 4X = 80$

18. a. $\Sigma X^2$
    b. $(\Sigma X)^2$

19. a. $\Sigma(X + 3)$
    b. $\Sigma X + 10$
    c. $\Sigma(X^2 - 2)$

20. a. $\Sigma X = -4$
    b. $\Sigma X^2 = 30$
    c. $\Sigma(X + 3) = 11$

21. a. $\Sigma X = 4.6$
    b. $\Sigma X^2 = 5.38$

22. a. $\Sigma X = -3$
    b. $\Sigma Y = 14$
    c. $\Sigma XY = -14$
    d. $\Sigma(Y - 1)^2 = 30$

23. a. $\Sigma X^2 = 175$
    b. $(\Sigma X)^2 = 625$
    c. $\Sigma(X + 2) = 35$
    d. $\Sigma(X + 1)^2 = 230$

24. a. $\Sigma X = 25$
    b. $\Sigma X^2 = 165$
    c. $(\Sigma X)^2 = 625$
    d. $\Sigma(X - 5)^2 = 40$

# CHAPTER 2:  FREQUENCY DISTRIBUTIONS

1.

| X | f | p | % |
|---|---|---|---|
| 5 | 3 | .15 | 15% |
| 4 | 4 | .20 | 20% |
| 3 | 8 | .40 | 40% |
| 2 | 3 | .15 | 15% |
| 1 | 2 | .10 | 10% |

2.

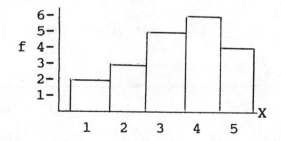 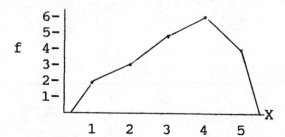

3.  $N = \Sigma f = 13$,   $\Sigma X = 38$,   $\Sigma X^2 = 128$

4.  A bar graph is used when the measurements are from a nominal or an ordinal scale.

5.  A grouped frequency distribution is used when the original scale of measurement consists of more categories than can be listed simply in a regular table.  Around 20 or more categories is generally considered too many for a regular table.

6.  The simplest and most complete way to present a set of
N = 7 scores is to list each individual score.  You would
need a grouped table to cover a range of 61 to 96, and the
grouped table would not tell you the exact value of each
score.  Also, a grouped table is more complicated than a
simple listing of the scores.

7.  In a grouped table you cannot determine the exact value
of each score.  For example, you may know that f = 7
individuals had scores in the interval from 80 to 89, but
you do not know the values for the actual scores.

8.

| X | f |
|---|---|
| 7 | 1 |
| 6 | 1 |
| 5 | 2 |
| 4 | 3 |
| 3 | 2 |
| 2 | 1 |

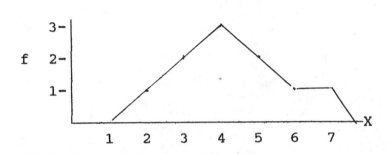

9.  a.  N = 14

    b.  $\Sigma X = 33$

10.  a.

| X | f |
|----|---|
| 10 | 1 |
| 9  | 0 |
| 8  | 1 |
| 7  | 3 |
| 6  | 1 |
| 5  | 2 |
| 4  | 5 |
| 3  | 4 |
| 2  | 2 |
| 1  | 1 |

b.

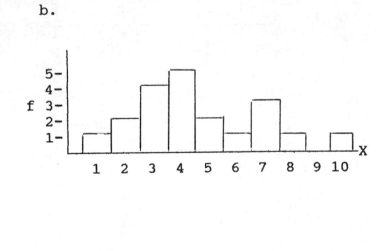

11.  The scores range from 112 to 816 and should be
presented in a grouped table.

| X | f |
|---|---|
| 800–899 | 1 |
| 700–799 | 3 |
| 600–699 | 4 |
| 500–599 | 6 |
| 400–499 | 5 |
| 300–399 | 3 |
| 200–299 | 1 |
| 100–199 | 1 |

12.

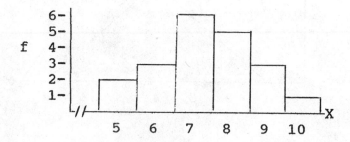

13.

| X | f |
|---|---|
| 30–31 | 1 |
| 28–29 | 2 |
| 26–27 | 2 |
| 24–25 | 3 |
| 22–23 | 5 |
| 20–21 | 5 |
| 18–19 | 5 |
| 16–17 | 3 |
| 14–15 | 1 |
| 12–13 | 1 |

| X | f |
|---|---|
| 30–34 | 1 |
| 25–29 | 5 |
| 20–24 | 12 |
| 15–19 | 8 |
| 10–14 | 2 |

14.  a.  The independent variable is diet.  The dependent variable is the number of errors on the discrimination task.

b.

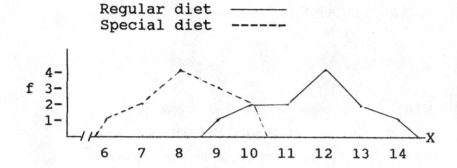

Regular diet ———
Special diet ------

c.  Yes, the diet appears to have an effect.  Error scores with the regular diet are consistently higher than scores with the special diet.

15.  a.

| X | f |
|---|---|
| 85–89 | 2 |
| 80–84 | 0 |
| 75–79 | 3 |
| 70–74 | 4 |
| 65–69 | 6 |
| 60–64 | 6 |
| 55–59 | 2 |
| 50–54 | 3 |
| 45–49 | 3 |
| 40–44 | 1 |

b.

| X | f |
|---|---|
| 80–89 | 2 |
| 70–79 | 7 |
| 60–69 | 12 |
| 50–59 | 5 |
| 40–49 | 4 |

16.

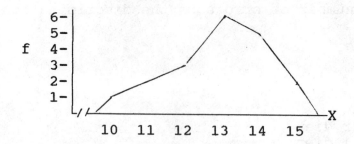

17.  a.  width = 2, need around 9 intervals

     b.  width = 5, need around 10 intervals

     c.  width = 50, need around 8 intervals

18.  a.

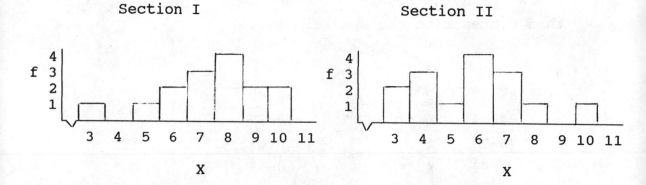

b.  The scores in Section I are centered around X = 8 and form a negatively skewed distribution.  In Section II, the scores are lower (centered around X = 6) and there is a tendency toward a positively skewed distribution.

19.

| X | f | p | % |
|---|---|---|---|
| 6 | 2 | .08 | 8% |
| 5 | 3 | .12 | 12% |
| 4 | 3 | .12 | 12% |
| 3 | 4 | .16 | 16% |
| 2 | 5 | .20 | 20% |
| 1 | 8 | .32 | 32% |

The distribution is positively skewed


20.  a.

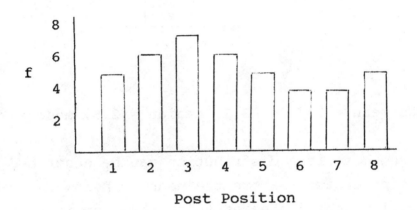

Post Position

b.  The distribution is essentially flat or rectangular.

c.  There is little evidence for any differences among the 8 positions.  However, post position 3 has produced more winners than any other.

# CHAPTER 3: CENTRAL TENDENCY

1.   Mean = 32/10 = 3.2
     Median = 3.5
     Mode = 4

2.   a.

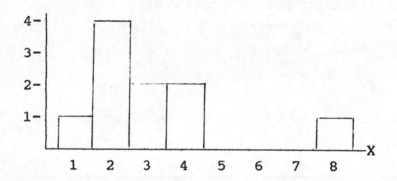

     b.   The mean = 31/10 = 3.1, median = 2.5, mode = 2.

3.   a.   Each score in a distribution can be described by
     its position either above the mean or below the mean.
     The total of the distances above the mean is exactly
     equal to the total of the distances below the mean, so
     the mean serves as a "balance point" for the set of
     scores.
     b.   Exactly 50% of the scores in a distribution are
     located above the median and exactly 50% are below the
     median.  Thus, the median divides the distribution
     exactly in half and the median serves as the "midpoint"
     of the distribution.

4.   The original $\Sigma X = 42$.  Removing $X = 12$ results in $n = 5$
     scores with $\Sigma X = 30$ and $\bar{X} = 6$.

5.  The original $\Sigma X = 90$.  With the additional score, n = 10 and $\Sigma X = 120$.  The new mean is $120/10 = 12$.

6.  The original $\Sigma X = 88$.  New $\Sigma X = 104$ and new $\mu = 13$.

7.  The median is used instead of the mean when there is a skewed distribution (few extreme scores), an open-ended distribution, undetermined scores, or an ordinal scale.

8.  a.  mode = 2
    b.  median = 2.5
    c.  You cannot find the total number of absences ($\Sigma X$) for this class.

9.  The mode is preferred when the scores are measured on a nominal scale.

10. The original samples have $\Sigma X = 12$ and $\Sigma X = 70$.  The combined sample has $\Sigma X = 82$ and n = 10.  The mean for the combined sample is $82/10 = 8.2$.

11. The mean = 5.9, median = 4.5, mode = 4.

12. The mean is displaced toward the tail of a skewed distribution so it often is not a good representative value.

13. Although the mean and median would be located in the center of the distribution, they would not be representative of most of the scores.  The individual scores would be clustered around the two modes with relatively few scores located in the center.

14.   The mean, median, and mode are identical for a symmetrical distribution with one mode.

15.   $\Sigma X = 1300$

16.   n = 64

17.   a.   The new mean is $\bar{X} = 120$   (6 times the old mean).
      b.   The new mean is $\bar{X} = 25$   (the old mean plus 5 points).

18.   The mean = 33/12 = 2.75, median = 2.5, mode = 2.

19.   a.   The mean = 41/9 = 4.56, median = 5.
      b.   The mean = 17/8 = 2.125, median = 1.5.

20.   The distribution is negatively skewed (the mean is displaced toward the tail of the distribution).

21.   a.   The mean = 7.19 and the median = 6.50.
      b.   Using the mean to describe the class average, the class is above the national norm.
      c.   Using the median to describe the class average, the class is below the national norm.

22.   a.   Independent variable is the brand of coffee. Dependent variable is the flavor rating.
      b.   Nominal
      c.   Bar graph

d.

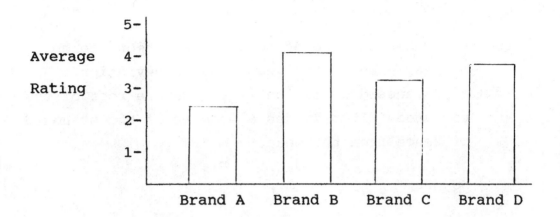

23.  a.  Independent variable is blood alcohol level.
     Dependent variable is reaction time.
     b.  Ratio scale
     c.  Histogram or line graph

     d.

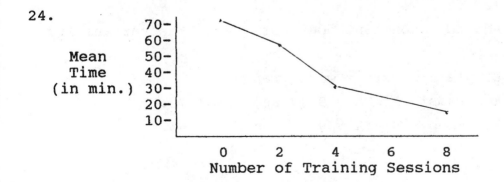

24.

# CHAPTER 4: VARIABILITY

1.  a.  SS is the sum of squared deviation scores
    b.  Variance is the mean squared deviation.
    c.  Standard deviation is the square root of the variance. It provides a measure of the standard distance from the mean.

2.  SS = 54, $\sigma^2$ = 9, $\sigma$ = 3

3.  SS = 20, $s^2$ = 5, s = 2.24

4.  SS = 9, $s^2$ = 3, s = 1.73

5.  a.  $\Sigma X$ = 300
    b.  $\Sigma(X - \mu)$ = 0   (always)
    c.  $\Sigma(X - \mu)^2$ = SS = 200

6.  a.  $\sigma$ = 0  (there are no deviations from the mean)
    b.  $\sigma$ = 1  (all scores are 1 point from the mean)

7.  The range = 12 points, Q1 = 3.5, and Q3 = 8.5. Semi-interquartile range = 2.5, SS = 120, s = 3.30.

8.  a.  All measures of variability are the same as in problem #7.
    b.  Adding a constant does not change the variability.

9.  a.  Sample B covers a wider range.
    b.  For sample A: $\bar{X}$ = 9.17 and s = 1.72.
    c.  For sample B: $\bar{X}$ = 9.00 and s = 5.66.

10. The standard deviation, $\sigma = 20$, provides a measure of the standard distance from the mean.

11. The scores range from 1 to 7, and the mean must be within this range. Thus, no score can deviate from the mean by more than 6 points, so the standard deviation must be less than 6.

12. SS cannot be less than zero because it is computed by adding squared deviations. Squared deviations are always greater than or equal to zero.

13. A standard deviation of zero means that there is no variability. All the scores have exactly the same value.

14. a. and b. $\mu = 4$

| X | $(X - \mu)$ |
|---|---|
| 1 | -3 |
| 6 | 2 |
| 9 | 5 |
| 0 | -4 |
| 4 | 0 |

$$0 = \Sigma(X - \mu)$$

c. SS = 9 + 4 + 25 + 16 + 0 = 54

d. You obtain exactly the same values (mean, deviations, and SS) whether the scores are a sample or a population.

15. a. $\bar{X} = 3$ definitional formula
    b. $\bar{X} = 3.2$ computational formula

16. The total of the deviation scores must be zero, so the "mystery person" has a deviation of −6. Therefore, the score for this person is X = 14.

17. a. College students $\bar{X}$ = 40.6 and business people $\bar{X}$ = 40.1. On average, both groups are very accurate.
    b. College students s = 9.22 and business people s = 2.56. Age estimates for the business men are generally close to the correct value. The estimates for the college students are much more scattered.

18. a.

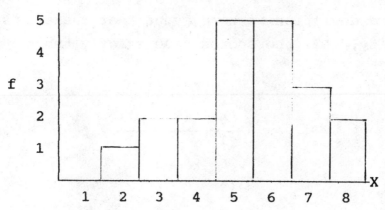

    b. Estimate $\mu$ = 5.5 and $\sigma$ = 1.5.
    c. $\mu$ = 5.4 and $\sigma$ = 1.59

19. a.

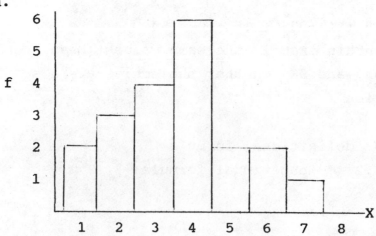

b. range = 7

c. interquartile range = (4.5 − 2.5) = 2

d. semi-interquartile range = 1

20. a. SS = 36, variance = 9, standard deviation = 3

b. SS = 36, variance = 9, standard deviation = 3

c. SS = 144, variance = 36, standard deviation = 6

d. Adding a constant to each score does not change any of the deivations and does not change the standard deviation.

e. When each score is multiplied by a constant, the deviations and the standard deviation are also multiplied by the constant.

21. $\sigma^2 = (3.5)^2 = 12.25$

22. a. The standard deviation is 10

b. SS = 2400

# CHAPTER 5: z-SCORES

1.  A z-score describes a precise location within a distribution. The sign of the z-score tells whether the location is above (+) or below (-) the mean, and the magnitude tells the distance from the mean in terms of the number of standard deviations.

2.  The distribution of z-scores will have the same shape (positively skewed) with a mean of 0 and a standard deviation of 1.

3.  The score X = 50 is more extreme when the variability is small ($\sigma$ = 20). In this case, X = 50 corresponds to a z-score of z = 2.50.

4.  Because the score, X = 55, is above the mean, $\mu$ = 45, it must have a positive z-score. Therefore, z = -2.00 cannot be correct.

5.  a.

| X | z | | X | z |
|---|---|---|---|---|
| 58 | 0.50 | | 46 | -0.25 |
| 34 | -1.00 | | 62 | 0.75 |
| 82 | 2.00 | | 74 | 1.50 |

   b.

| X | z | | X | z |
|---|---|---|---|---|
| 90 | 2.50 | | 54 | 0.25 |
| 42 | -0.50 | | 34 | -1.00 |
| 26 | -1.50 | | 62 | 0.75 |

6.  a.

| X | z | | X | z |
|---|---|---|---|---|
| 106 | 0.60 | | 90 | -1.00 |
| 125 | 2.50 | | 87 | -1.30 |
| 93 | -0.70 | | 118 | 1.80 |

b.

| X | z | | X | z |
|---|---|---|---|---|
| 112 | 1.20 | | 94 | -0.60 |
| 123 | 2.30 | | 104 | 0.40 |
| 92 | -0.80 | | 70 | -3.00 |

7.

| X | z | | X | z |
|---|---|---|---|---|
| 40 | 1.00 | | 29 | -1.20 |
| 42 | 1.40 | | 47 | 2.40 |
| 34 | -0.20 | | 26 | -1.80 |

8.

| X | z | | X | z |
|---|---|---|---|---|
| 110 | 1.25 | | 97 | 0.60 |
| 39 | -2.30 | | 77 | -0.40 |
| 55 | -1.50 | | 127 | 2.10 |

9.  $\sigma = 6$

10. $\sigma = 4$

11. $\mu = 45$

12. $\mu = 80$

13. $\mu = 55$ and $\sigma = 5$

14. $\sigma = 8$ gives $z = +1.00$ (better score)
    $\sigma = 16$ gives $z = +0.50$

15. $\sigma = 8$ gives $z = -1.00$
    $\sigma = 16$ gives $z = -0.50$ (better score)

16. For psychology, z = +0.50. For English, z = +2.00. The z-score of +2.00 (English test) indicates a much higher position within the distribution than the z-score of 0.50 (psychology test). You should expect a better grade in English.

17.

| Student | z-score | X-value |
|---------|---------|---------|
| Ramon | 2.00 | 110 |
| Jill | 1.20 | 102 |
| Sharon | 0.90 | 99 |
| Steve | 0.50 | 95 |

18. a. $\mu = 6$ and $\sigma = 4$

   b.

| X | z | X | z |
|----|-------|---|-------|
| 12 | 1.50 | 3 | -0.75 |
| 1 | -1.25 | 7 | 0.25 |
| 10 | 1.00 | 3 | -0.75 |

19. a. For this population, $\mu = 7$ and $\sigma = 4$.
   b.

| X | z | X | z |
|----|-------|---|-------|
| 14 | 1.75 | 5 | -0.50 |
| 11 | 1.00 | 8 | 0.25 |
| 1 | -1.50 | 7 | 0 |
| 4 | -0.75 | 3 | -1.00 |
| 12 | 1.25 | 5 | -0.50 |

20. The numerator of the z-score formula is a deviation score, $X - \mu$. Deviation scores always sum to zero.

21.

| Raw Score | Standardized Score |
|-----------|--------------------|
| 41        | 13.0               |
| 32        | 8.5                |
| 38        | 11.5               |
| 44        | 14.5               |
| 45        | 15.0               |
| 36        | 10.5               |
| 27        | 6.0                |

22.  a.  $\mu = 5$ and $\sigma = 2$

b.

| X | z     |
|---|-------|
| 8 | 1.50  |
| 6 | 0.50  |
| 2 | −1.50 |
| 4 | −0.50 |
| 5 | 0     |

c.

| original X | new X |
|------------|-------|
| 8          | 130   |
| 6          | 110   |
| 2          | 70    |
| 4          | 90    |
| 5          | 100   |

# CHAPTER 6: PROBABILITY

1.  a.  p = 45/60 = 0.75
    b.  p = 25/60 = 0.42
    c.  p =  5/60 = 0.08


2.  a.  p = 20/30
    b.  p = 10/30 (Remember, a <u>random</u> sample requires replacement.


3.  a.  left = 0.8413, right = 0.1587
    b.  left = 0.0668, right = 0.9332
    c.  left = 0.5987, right = 0.4013
    d.  left = 0.3085, right = 0.6915


4.  a.  0.3085
    b.  0.0401
    c.  0.0668
    d.  0.4013


5.  a.  z = 0.25
    b.  z = 1.28
    c.  z = -0.84


6.  a.  z = 0.50, left = 0.6915, right = 0.3085
    b.  z = 0, left = 0.5000, right = 0.5000
    c.  z = -0.20, left = 0.4207, right = 0.5793
    d.  z = -1.00, left = 0.1587, right = 0.8413


7.  a.  z = 0.52, X = 552
    b.  z = 0.67, X = 567
    c.  z = -1.28, X = 372

8.   a.   z = +0.25,   X = 125
     b.   z = +1.28,   X = 145.6
     c.   z between -0.84 and +0.84; X between 103.2 and
     136.8


9.   a.   z = 0.25, p = 0.4013
     b.   z = -0.25, p = 0.5987
     c.   z = 0.50, p = 0.6915
     d.   z = -0.50, p = 0.3085


10.  a.   z between +0.67 and -0.67,   p = 0.4972
     b.   z between 1.33 and 2.00,   p = 0.0690


11.  Converted to z-scores, the correct order is:
           John   z = +0.75   highest
           Tom    z = +0.50   middle
           Mary   z = +0.25   lowest


12.  a.   z = 2.05,   X = 705
     b.   z = 0.52,   X = 552
     c.   z = 1.30,   percentile rank = 90.32%
     d.   z boundaries +1.96 and -1.96;   score boundaries 304
     and 696
     e.   Semi-interquartile range is 67 points (z boundaries
     for the interquartile range are +0.67 and -0.67).


13.  You cannot find the probability.  You cannot use the
     Unit Normal Table because the distribution is not
     normal.

14.  a.   The semi-interquartile range is bounded by $z = 0.67$
         and $z = -0.67$.  With $\sigma = 10$, the semi-interquartile
         range is $(0.67)(10) = 6.7$.
         b.   With $\sigma = 20$, the semi-interquartile range is
         $(0.67)(20) = 13.4$.
         c.   In general, the semi-interquartile range is equal
         to $0.67\sigma$.

15.  a.   Bill's z-score is $z = +0.92$ and his percentile rank
         is 82.12%.  If he were in the pre-engineering section
         his z-score would $z = +0.25$ and his percentile rank
         would be 59.87%.
         b.   A percentile rank of 40% corresponds to $z = -0.25$
         or $X = 70$.  In the humanities section a score of $X = 70$
         corresponds to $z = +0.58$ and a percentile rank of
         71.90%.
         c.   Mary's score is $X = 66$.  Jane's score is $X = 68$.

16.  The bottom 25% have z-scores less than $-0.67$ or scores
     less than 63.  The top 25% have z-scores greater than
     $+0.67$ or scores greater than 73.  The middle 50% have
     scores between 63 and 73.

17.  a.   $z = +0.84$ or $X = 116.8$
         b.   $z = +0.40$ so the percentage is 34.46%

18.  $p(X > 25 \text{ minutes}) = p(z > = -0.50) = 0.6915$

19.  a.   $p = 0.6915$
         b.   $p = 0.0668$
         c.   $p = 0.9772$
         d.   $p = 0.8664$

20. a. z = 1.28, X = 264

    b. z = -0.52, X = 174

    c. z = 0.67, X = 233.5


21. a. z = 0.50, percentile rank = 69.15%

    b. z = 1.50, percentile rank = 93.32%

    c. z = -0.50, percentile rank = 30.85%

    d. z = -1.50, percentile rank = 6.68%


22. a. z = 1.25, percentile rank = 89.44%

    b. z = -0.88, percentile rank = 18.94%

    c. z = 2.38, percentile rank = 99.13%


23. a. z = 1.04, X = 68.32

    b. z = 0.25, X = 62

    c. z = -0.84, X = 53.28


24. a. Q1: z = -0.67, X = 79.90

       Q2: z = 0, X = 100

       Q3: z = 0.67, X = 120.10

    b. interquartile range = 120.10 - 79.90 = 40.20

       semi-interquartile range = 20.1

# CHAPTER 7:  PROBABILITY AND SAMPLES: THE DISTRIBUTION OF SAMPLE MEANS

1.  a.   The distribution of sample means is the set of all possible sample means for random samples of a specific size (n) from a specific population.
    b.   The expected value of $\bar{X}$ is the mean of the distribution of sample means ($\mu$).
    c.   The standard error of $\bar{X}$ is the standard deviation of the distribution of sample means ($\sigma_{\bar{x}} = \sigma/\sqrt{n}$).

2.  The larger sample (n = 30) will have the smaller standard error.  On average, $\bar{X}$ from the larger sample will be closer to $\mu$.

3.  a.   Standard deviation, $\sigma = 30$, measures the standard distance between a score and the population mean.
    b.   The standard error, $\sigma_{\bar{x}} = 30/\sqrt{100} = 3$, measures the standard distance between a sample mean and the population mean.

4.  a.   Standard error = $100/\sqrt{4} = 50$
    b.   Standard error = $100/\sqrt{25} = 20$
    c.   Standard error = $100/\sqrt{100} = 10$

5.  a.   z = +2.00
    b.   z = -2.00
    c.   z = +1.20

6.  a.   Standard error = 6, z = 1.00, p = 0.1587 (more likely)
    b.   Standard error = 2, z = 1.50, p = 0.0668

7.  a.  #1 standard error = 10, z = +1.00;  #2 standard error = 4, z = +1.25;  #3 standard error = 2, z = +2.00
    b.  Sample #3 is the most extreme and therefore the least likely of the three.

8.  a.  z = -0.50,  p = 0.3085
    b.  Standard error = 10, z = -1.00, p = 0.1587
    c.  Standard error = 4, z = -2.50, p = 0.0062

9.  a.  z = +1.00,  p = 0.1587
    b.  z = -2.00,  p = 0.0228

10. a.  $\sigma_{\bar{x}}$ = 10, z = 0.50, p = 0.3085
    b.  $\sigma_{\bar{x}}$ = 5, z = 1.00, p = 0.1587
    c.  $\sigma_{\bar{x}}$ = 2, z = 2.50, p = 0.0062

11. a.  With n = 4 the distribution of sample means will not be normal and you cannot use the unit normal table to find the answer.
    b.  With n = 36 the distribution of sample means will be normal.  $\sigma_{\bar{x}}$ = 3, z = 1.00, p = 0.1587.

12. a.  $\sigma_{\bar{x}}$ = 6, p(-0.83 < z < 0.83) = 0.5934
    b.  $\sigma_{\bar{x}}$ = 3, p(-1.67 < z < 1.67) = 0.9050

13. a.  The distribution of sample means is normal with $\mu$ = 80 and $\sigma_{\bar{x}}$ = 3.
    b.  z = 1.67, p = 0.0475
    c.  p(76 < $\bar{X}$ < 84) = p(-1.33 < z < 1.33) = 0.8164
    d.  z = 1.00, p = 0.8413
    e.  z = -2.00, p = 0.0228

14. a.  n > 4
    b.  n > 16
    c.  n > 400

15.   n = 25

16.   a.   With a standard error of 3.41 this sample mean
      corresponds to a z-score of z = 3.43.   A z-score this
      extreme has a probability of only p = 0.0003.
      b.   It would be almost impossible to obtain a sample
      mean this large by random sampling.

17.   With n = 16, $\sigma_{\bar{x}}$ = 0.50, $p(\bar{X} \leq 31) = p(z \leq -2.00)$ =
      0.0228.   This is a very unlikely outcome by chance
      alone.   The inspector should suspect some problem with
      the machinery.

18.   a.   With n = 4, $\sigma_{\bar{x}}$ = 1, and z = -2.00.   The probability
      of obtaining a value this small or smaller is p =
      0.0228.
      b.   The result is very unlikely to occur by chance (p =
      0.0228).   The manager has reason to suspect that he has
      been cheated.

19.   a.

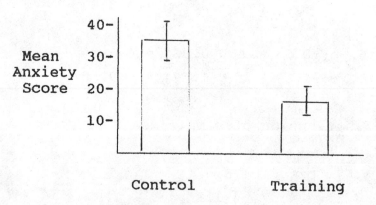

      b.   Even considering the standard error for each mean,
      there is no overlap between the two groups.   The
      relaxation training does seem to have lowered scores
      more than would be expected by chance.

20.  a.

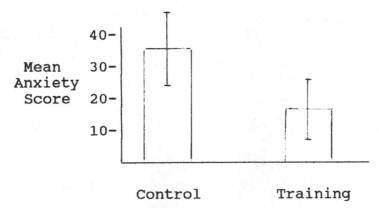

b.  Considering the standard error for each group, the mean for the control group could be a low as 24 and the mean for the training group could be as high as 28. There is overlap between the two groups when the error is considered so you cannot be certain that the training worked.

21.

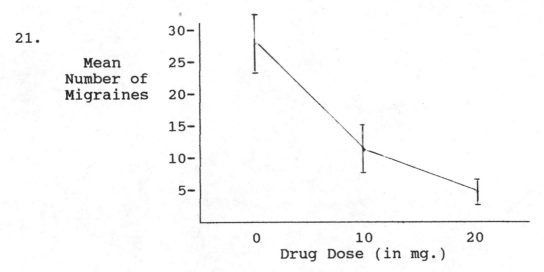

22.  a.  The distribution of sample means is normal with $\mu = 90$ and $\sigma_{\bar{x}} = 3$.

b.  The middle 95% corresponds to z-scores between 1.96 and -1.96, or sample means between 95.88 and 84.12.

c.  The middle 99% corresponds to z-scores between 2.58 and -2.58, or sample means between 97.74 and 82.26.

23.  a.

| Sample | 1st | 2nd | $\bar{X}$ |
|--------|-----|-----|-----------|
| #1 | 0 | 0 | 0 |
| #2 | 0 | 2 | 1 |
| #3 | 0 | 4 | 2 |
| #4 | 2 | 0 | 1 |
| #5 | 2 | 2 | 2 |

| Sample | 1st | 2nd | $\bar{X}$ |
|--------|-----|-----|-----------|
| #6 | 2 | 4 | 3 |
| #7 | 4 | 0 | 2 |
| #8 | 4 | 2 | 3 |
| #9 | 4 | 4 | 4 |

b.

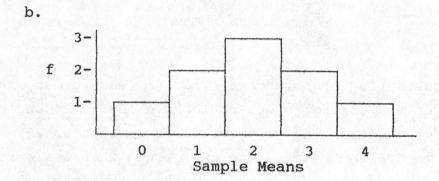

# CHAPTER 8: INTRODUCTION TO HYPOTHESIS TESTING

1.  a.  Independent variable is presense or absense of the hormone.  Dependent variable is weight at 10 weeks of age.

    b.  The null hypothesis states that the growth hormone will have no effect on the weight of rats at 10 weeks of age.

    c.  $H_0$: $\mu = 950$       $H_1$: $\mu \neq 950$

    d.  The critical region consists of z-score values beyond 1.96 or -1.96 in a normal distribution.

    e.  For this sample $\sigma_{\bar{x}} = 6$ and z = 4.00.

    f.  Reject the null hypothesis and conclude that the hormone has a significant effect on weight.


2.  a. $H_0$:  $\mu = 500$.  The critical boundaries are z = ±1.96.  For these data, z = 2.16, so our decision is to reject $H_0$ and conclude that the course did affect SAT scores.

    b.  With  $\alpha = .01$, the critical region consists of z-score values greater than 2.58 or less than -2.58. The decision is fail to reject $H_0$.

    c.  With  $\alpha = .01$ there is less risk of a Type I Error. Therefore, the test requires a larger treatment effect in order to reject $H_0$.  In this case the discrepancy between the data and the hypothesis  (554 versus 500) is sufficient to reject $H_0$ for $\alpha = .05$ but not for $\alpha = .01$.

3.  a. $\bar{X} - \mu$ measures the difference between the sample data and the null hypothesis.
    b. A sample mean is not expected to be identical to the population mean. The standard error indicates how much difference between $\bar{X}$ and $\mu$ is expected by chance.

4.  a. A Type I Error is rejecting a true $H_0$. This can occur if you obtain a very unusual sample with scores that are much different from the general population.
    b. A Type II Error is failing to reject a false $H_0$. This can happen when the treatment effect is very small. In this case the treated sample is not noticeably different from the original population.

5.  A smaller alpha level (e.g., .01 versus .05) has the advantage of reducing the risk of a Type I error. That is, when you reject the null hypothesis you are more confident that you have made the correct decision. On the other hand, a smaller alpha level makes it more difficult to reject $H_0$. That is, a small alpha level requires a large discrepancy between the data and the null hypothesis before you can say that a significant difference exists.

6.  The null hypothesis states that the price change has no effect on weekly sales: $H_0$: $\mu = 185$. For these data, the standard error is 7, and the z-score statistic is -1.71. Fail to reject the null hypothesis and conclude that there has been no significant change in weekly sales.

7.    The null hypothesis states that the mean IQ for children whose mothers had German measles is no different from the general population mean, $\mu = 100$. For this sample mean z = -0.90 if the null hypothesis is true. Fail to reject the null hypothesis.

8.    a.  For n = 25, $\sigma_{\bar{x}} = 2$ and z = 1.50. Fail to reject the null hypothesis. There is no significant difference in vocabulary skills between only-children and the general population.
      b.  For n = 100, $\sigma_{\bar{x}} = 1$ and z = 3.00. Reject the null hypothesis and conclude there is a significant difference in vocabulary skills between only-children and the general population.
      c.  The larger sample results in a smaller standard error. With n = 100 the difference between the data and the null hypothesis is significantly more than could be explained by chance.

9.    For this sample $\sigma_{\bar{x}} = 0.32$ and z = -4.06. Reject $H_0$ and conclude there has been a significant change in homework hours.

10.   For the one-tailed test, the null hypothesis states that there is no memory impairment, $H_0$: $\mu \geq 50$. The critical region consists of z-scores less than -1.65. For these data $\sigma_{\bar{x}} = 1.28$ and z = -2.34. Reject $H_0$ and conclude the alcoholics have significantly lower memory scores.

11.   For this sample $\sigma_{\bar{x}} = 0.077$ and z = 4.68. Reject $H_0$ and conclude there has been a significant change in GPA.

12.  a.  For the one-tailed test, $H_0: \mu \leq 55$ (there is no increase in depression). With $\alpha = .05$ the critical region consists of z-score values greater than 1.65. The data have $\sigma_{\bar{x}} = 2$ and $z = 2.00$. Reject $H_0$ and conclude that the elderly subjects are significantly more depressed.

b.  With $\alpha = .01$ the critical region consists of z-score values greater than 2.33. Fail to reject $H_0$.

c.  Lowering $\alpha$ from .05 to .01 requires more evidence to reject the null hypothesis. The data in this study were sufficient to reject $H_0$ with $\alpha = .05$ but not with $\alpha = .01$.


13.  a.  $H_0: \mu = 65$.  $\sigma_{\bar{x}} = 4$ and $z = -1.25$. Fail to reject $H_0$.

b.  $H_0: \mu = 55$.  $\sigma_{\bar{x}} = 4$ and $z = 1.25$. Fail to reject $H_0$.

c.  With a sample mean of $\bar{X} = 60$ it is reasonable to expect that the population mean has a value near 60. Any value that is reasonably near to 60 will be an acceptable hypothesis for $\mu$. The standard error and the alpha level determine the range of acceptable values.


14.  a.  A researcher can reduce the risk of a Type I error by lowering the alpha level for the hypothesis test.

b.  A researcher can reduce the standard error by taking a larger sample (increasing n).

15. The analyses are contradictory. The critical region for the two-tailed tests consists of the extreme 2.5% in each tail of the distribution. The two-tailed conclusion indicates that the data were not in this critical region. However, the one-tailed test indicates that the data were in the extreme 1% of one tail. Data cannot be in the extreme 1% and at the same time fail to be in the extreme 2.5%.

16. a. For the one-tailed test, $H_0$: $\mu \leq 100$ (IQ's are not above average). With $\alpha = .05$ the critical region consists of z-score values greater than 1.65. The data have $\sigma_{\bar{x}} = 3$ and z = 1.67. Reject $H_0$ and conclude that the first-born subjects have significantly higher IQ's.
   b. For the two-tailed test, $H_0$: $\mu = 100$ (IQ's are not different from average). With $\alpha = .05$ the critical region consists of z-score values beyond 1.96 or −1.96. The data produce z = 1.67 which is not in the critical region. Fail to reject $H_0$ and conclude that IQ's for first-born subjects are not significantly different from the general population.

17. a. The null hypothesis states that the training program has no effect on the problem solving scores ($H_0$: $\mu = 80$). For these data, the standard error is 2.36 and z = 1.88. Fail to reject $H_0$. There is not sufficient evidence to conclude that the training program has any effect.
   b. For a one-tailed test the z-score is in the critical region and the decision is to reject $H_0$.

18. $H_0$: $\mu \geq 20$ (not reduced), and $H_1$: $\mu < 20$ (reduced). For these data the standard error is 1 and the z-score is z = −4.50. Reject $H_0$.

19. For the one-tailed test, $H_0$: $\mu \geq 80$ (not lower self-esteem). With $\alpha = .05$ the critical region consists of z-score values less than -1.65. The data have $\sigma_{\bar{x}} = 3$ and $z = -1.33$. Fail to reject $H_0$ and conclude that the children from divorced families do not have significantly lower self-esteem scores.

20. a. $H_0$: $\mu = 100$ (Oxygen deprivation has no effect on IQ). With $\alpha = .05$ the critical region consists of z-score values greater than +1.96 or less than -1.96. For these data, $\bar{X} = 90.73$ and $z = -2.40$. Reject the null hypothesis. Oxygen deprivation at birth does have a significant effect on IQ.

b. With $\alpha = .01$ the critical boundaries change to $z = \pm 2.58$, and the decision would be fail to reject the null hypothesis.

# CHAPTER 9: INTRODUCTION TO THE t-STATISTIC

1.  The t statistic is used when the population standard deviation is unknown.  You use the sample data to estimate the standard deviation and the standard error.

2.  The sample standard deviation, s, provides an estimate of the unknown population standard deviation, $\sigma$.  That is, s estimates the standard distance between the mean and an individual score or X-value.  The estimated standard error, $s_{\bar{x}}$, estimates the standard distance between the population mean and the sample mean.  The estimated standard error depends, in part, on the sample size; the larger the sample, the smaller the error.

3.  The t statistic assumes random sampling from a normal distribution.

4.  The standard deviation (s) in the t formula is an estimated value and contributes to the variability.

5.  As df increase the t distribution becomes less variable (less spread out) and more like a normal distribution. For $\alpha$ = .05, the critical t values move toward $\pm1.96$ as df increases.

6.   The null hypothesis states that self-esteem for the
     athletes is not different from self-esteem for the
     general population.  In symbols, $H_0$: $\mu$ = 70.  For these
     data, $s_{\bar{x}}$ = 2 and t(24) = 1.50 which is not beyond the
     critical boundaries of t = ±2.064.  Fail to reject the
     null hypothesis.

7.   $H_0$:  $\mu$ = 7.9 (no change from 10 years ago).  For these
     data, $s_{\bar{x}}$ = 0.10 and t(99) = -6.00 which is in the
     critical region beyond t = ±2.660.  Reject $H_0$.

8.   a.  $H_0$:  $\mu \leq$ 70 (not better), and $H_1$:  $\mu >$ 70 (better).
     With df = 15 the critical region consists of t values
     greater than 1.753.  For these data, t = 6/2 = 3.00.
     Reject $H_0$ and conclude that performance is
     significantly better in the afternoon.
     b.  The independent variable is time of class and the
     dependent variable is the final exam score.

9.   a.  With n = 25 the standard error is 2.00 and the t
     statistic is t(24) = -2.00.  Fail to reject $H_0$.
     b.  With n = 400 the standard error is 0.50 and the t
     statistic is t(399) = -8.00.  Reject $H_0$.
     c.  The larger the sample, the smaller the standard
     error (denominator of the t-statistic).  If other
     factors are held constant, a smaller standard error
     will produce a larger t statistic which is more likely
     to be significant.

10.  a.  Your sketch should show a normal distribution
     centered at X = 55 with a standard deviation of s = 2.
     The hypothesized mean, $\mu$ = 50, is located far in the
     tail of the distribution.  It does not appear that the
     sample distribution is centered around $\mu$ = 50.

b.  $H_0$:  $\mu = 50$.  For these data the standard error is 0.50 and $t(15) = 10.00$.  Reject $H_0$ and conclude that the population mean is significantly different from $\mu = 50$.  This conclusion is consistent with the sketch in part a.

c.  Your sketch should show a normal distribution centered at X = 55 with a standard deviation of s = 20. The hypothesized mean, $\mu = 50$, is located near the center of the distribution.  Because the sample is centered around $\mu = 50$, it appears that $\mu = 50$ is a reasonable value for the population mean.

d.  $H_0$:  $\mu = 50$.  With SS = 6000 the standard error is 5.00 and $t(15) = 1.00$.   Fail to reject $H_0$ and conclude that the population mean is not significantly different from $\mu = 50$.  This conclusion is consistent with the sketch in part a.

11.  a.  $H_0$:  $\mu = 5.00$.  With a standard error of 0.10, $t(24) = 2.00$ which is not beyond the two-tailed critical boundaries of $t = \pm2.064$.  Fail to reject $H_0$ and conclude that the average weight is not significantly different from 5 pounds.

b.  $H_0$:  $\mu \leq 5.00$ (not more than 5 pounds).  With a one-tailed test, the critical boundary is $t = 1.711$. The obtained statistic, $t(24) = 2.00$, is in the critical region.  Reject $H_0$ and conclude that the average weight is significantly more than 5 pounds.

12.  $H_0$: $\mu = 21$.  With a standard error of 0.50, $t(99) = -4.60$ which is beyond the critical boundaries of $t = \pm2.00$.  Reject $H_0$ and conclude that humidity has a significant effect on the rats eating behavior.

13. $H_0$: $\mu$ = 40. For these data, s = 12, the standard error is 2.00, and t(35) = 2.25 which is beyond the critical boundaries of t = ±2.042. Reject $H_0$ and conclude that depression for the elderly is significantly different from depression for the general population.

14. $H_0$: $\mu \leq 60$ (not more pleasant), $H_1$: $\mu > 60$ (more pleasant) For these data, s = 5.00, the standard error is 1.00, and t(24) = 4.30 which is beyond the critical boundary of 1.711. Reject $H_0$ and conclude that memories for older adults are significantly more pleasant than memories for college students.

15. $H_0$: $\mu$ = 5.0. $\overline{X}$ = 6.3 and s = 2.03. With a standard error of 0.11, t(326) = 11.82 which is beyond the critical boundaries of t = ±2.617. Reject $H_0$.

16. $H_0$: $\mu \geq 15$. For these data, $\overline{X}$ = 11.71, s = 3.50, the standard error is 1.32, and t(6) = -2.49 which is beyond the one-tailed critical boundary of t = -1.943. Reject $H_0$ and conclude right hemisphere brain damage does significantly reduce spatial skills.

17. $H_0$: $\mu$ = 27. For these data $\overline{X}$ = 24.58, s = 3.48, and the standard error is 1.01. t(11) = -2.40 which is beyond the critical boundaries of t = ±2.201. Reject $H_0$ and conclude that the data are significantly different from the therapist's claim.

18. $H_0$: $\mu \leq 25$ (not more than $25). For these data, $\overline{X}$ = $28.00, s = 14.18, the standard error is 4.49, and t(9) = 0.67. Fail to reject $H_0$. The average donation is not significantly greater than $25.00.

19. $H_0$: $\mu \leq 20$ (not more than chance). For these data, $\bar{X} =$ 22.22, s = 4.18, the standard error is 1.39, and t(8) = 1.60. Fail to reject $H_0$. The performance for this sample is not significantly better than chance.

# CHAPTER 10: HYPOTHESIS TESTS WITH TWO INDEPENDENT SAMPLES

1.  a.  A single-sample t would be used.

    b.  An independent-measures hypothesis test to examine the difference between two populations.

    c.  An independent-measures t would be used to evaluate the difference between the two treatments.

2.  The standard error for the independent measures t provides an estimate of the standard distance between a sample mean difference $(\bar{X}_1 - \bar{X}_2)$ and the population mean difference $(\mu_1 - \mu_2)$. When the two samples come from the same population (when $H_0$ is true), the standard error indicates the standard amount of error (distance) between the two sample means.

3.  The pooled variance is 80, the standard error is 4, and $t(18) = 2.00$. For a one-tailed test, the critical value is $t = 1.734$. Reject $H_0$ and conclude that the traditional subjects are significantly more depressed than the androgynous subjects.

4.  The pooled variance is 60, the standard error is 3, and $t(28) = 2.33$. With $\alpha = .01$ the critical region consists of t values beyond $\pm 2.763$. Fail to reject $H_0$ and conclude that there is no significant difference in self-esteem between the two groups.

5.  a.  There is a total of 26 subjects in the two samples
    combined.
    b.  With df = 24 and $\alpha$ = .05 the critical region
    consists of t values beyond ±2.064.  The t statistic is
    in the critical region.  Reject $H_0$ and conclude that
    there is a significant difference.
    c.  With df = 24 and $\alpha$ = .01 the critical region
    consists of t values beyond ±2.797.  The t statistic is
    not in the critical region.  Fail to reject $H_0$ and
    conclude that there is no significant difference.

6.  Both experiments show a 10-point difference between the
    two sample means.  However, the variability in
    Experiment II is substantially greater than in
    Experiment I.  The smaller variability is Experiment I
    will make the mean difference more apparent, and is
    more likely to produce a significant t statistic.

7.  The pooled variance is 500, the standard error is 10,
    and t(18) = 1.30.  With $\alpha$ = .05 the critical region
    consists of t values beyond ±2.101.  Fail to reject $H_0$
    and conclude that there is no significant difference in
    political attitudes for freshmen versus seniors.

8.  The pooled variance is 30, the standard error is 3, and
    t(13) = 0.50.  Fail to reject $H_0$.

9.  a.  $H_0$: $\mu$ = 60  (no effect).  The data from sample 1
    produce a t statistic of t(8) = -2.00.  Fail to reject
    $H_0$.  The mean for Treatment A is not significantly
    different from 60.
    b.  $H_0$: $\mu$ = 60 (no effect).  The data from sample 2
    produce a t statistic of t(8) = 2.00.  Fail to reject
    $H_0$. The mean for Treatment B is not significantly
    different from 60.

c. $H_0$: $\mu_1 - \mu_2 = 0$ (no difference between treatments A and B). The pooled variance is 9 and the test statistic is $t(16) = -2.84$ which is beyond the critical boundaries of $t = \pm 2.120$. Reject $H_0$ and conclude that there is a significant difference between the two treatments.

d. The results are not contradictory. Treatment A produces a mean that is less than 60, but not enough to be significantly less. Treatment B produces a mean greater than 60, but not enough to be significantly greater. Each treatment appears to have a small (nonsignificant) effect, and the effects are in opposite directions. When the two small effects are combined in the independent-measures test, the result is a significant difference.

10. a. The pooled variance is 40 and $t(38) = -4.15$ which is beyond the critical boundaries of $t = \pm 2.042$. Reject $H_0$ and conclude that there is a significant difference between the two strategies.

b. The two sample variances are 51.05 and 28.95. F-max = 1.76. Fail to reject $H_0$ and conclude that there is no evidence of different variances.

11. $H_0$: $(\mu_1 - \mu_2) \leq 0$ (no increase). $H_1$: $(\mu_1 - \mu_2) > 0$ (increase). Pooled variance = 30 and $t(13) = 3.67$ which is beyond the one-tailed critical boundary of $t = 1.771$. Reject $H_0$ and conclude that fatigue has a significant effect.

12. The pooled variance is 20, the standard error is 2, and $t(18) = 1.50$. With $\alpha = .05$ the critical region consists of t values beyond $\pm 2.101$. Fail to reject $H_0$ and conclude that there is no significant difference in test scores between the two groups.

13. The pooled variance is 100, the standard error is 5, and $t(14) = 2.60$. With $\alpha = .01$ the critical region consists of t values beyond $\pm2.977$. Fail to reject $H_0$ and conclude that there is no significant difference in frustration scores between the two personality groups.

14. Pooled variance = 540 and $t(28) = -3.67$ which is beyond the $\alpha = .01$ critical boundaries of $t = \pm2.763$. Reject $H_0$ and conclude that pollution has a significant effect on life expectancy.

15. a.

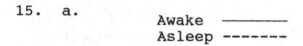

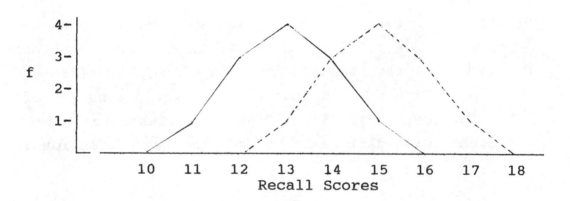

Recall Scores

b. For the asleep group $\bar{X} = 15$ and SS = 14. For the awake group $\bar{X} = 13$ and SS = 14. $t(22) = 4.35$ which is beyond the critical boundaries of $t = \pm2.074$. Reject $H_0$.

16. For the control group, $\bar{X} = 11.14$ and SS = 56.86. For the dog owners, $\bar{X} = 6.4$ and SS = 17.2. The pooled variance is 7.41 and $t(10) = 2.98$ which is beyond the critical boundaries of $t = \pm2.228$. Reject $H_0$. The data show a significant difference between the dog owners and the control group.

17. For the control group, $\bar{X} = 20.5$ and SS = 240. For the acupuncture group, $\bar{X} = 11.125$ and SS = 404.88. The pooled variance is 46.06 and t(14) = 2.77 which is beyond the critical boundaries of t = ±2.145. Reject $H_0$. The data indicate a significant difference between the acupuncture condition and the control group.

18. For the rich rats, $\bar{X} = 26.0$ and SS = 214. For the poor rats, $\bar{X} = 34.2$ and SS = 313.60. The pooled variance is 29.31, the standard error is 2.42, and t(18) = -3.39. With $\alpha$ = .01 the critical region consists of t values beyond ±2.878. Reject $H_0$. The data indicate a significant difference between the two environments.

19. For the artists, $\bar{X} = 7.071$ and SS = 36.91. For the pilots, $\bar{X} = 3.143$ and SS = 27.71. The pooled variance is 2.485, the standard error is 0.595, and t(26) = 6.60. With $\alpha$ = .05 the critical region consists of t values beyond ±2.056. Reject $H_0$. The data indicate a significant difference between the two professions.

20. $H_0$: $(\mu_1 - \mu_2) \geq 0$ (seniors not higher). $H_1$: $(\mu_1 - \mu_2) < 0$ (seniors are higher). For the sophomores, $\bar{X} = 21.2$ and SS = 261.20. For the seniors, $\bar{X} = 22.15$ and SS = 246.55. t(38) = -0.82. Fail to reject $H_0$. There is no evidence of a significant difference.

21. a. For treatment 1, $\bar{X} = 2.83$ with SS = 1.04. For treatment 2, $\bar{X} = 2.03$ with SS = 0.64. The pooled variance = 0.093 and the standard error is 0.136. t(18) = 5.88 which is beyond the critical boundaries of t = ±2.101. Reject $H_0$ and conclude that there is a significant difference between the two treatments.

b.  When each score is multiplied by 60, the sample
means and the sample standard deviations also will be
multiplied by 60.  However, the t statistic and the
statistical decision should not change because the data
have not actually been changed.

c.  You should still obtain  t(18) = 5.88.

# CHAPTER 11: HYPOTHESIS TESTS WITH TWO RELATED SAMPLES

1.  a.  This is an independent measures experiment with two separate samples.
    b.  This is repeated measures. The same sample is measured twice.
    c.  This is a matched subjects design. The repeated measures t statistic is appropriate.

2.  The primary advantage of a repeated-measures design over an independent-measures design is that the repeated-measures study eliminates variability due to individual differences. This usually results in smaller variability and produces a smaller standard error which increases the likelihood of detecting a difference.

3.  For a repeated-measures design the same subjects are used in both treatment conditions. In a matched-subjects design, two different sets of subjects are used. However, in a matched-subjects design, each subject in one condition is matched with respect to a specific variable with a subject in the second condition so that the two separate samples are equivalent with respect to the matching variable.

4.    a.    An independent-measures design would require two
      separate samples, each with 10 subjects, for a total of
      20 subjects.
      b.    A repeated-measures design would use the same
      sample of n = 10 subjects in both treatment conditions.
      c.    A matched-subjects design would require two
      separate samples with n = 10 in each, for a total of 20
      subjects.

5.    The null hypothesis says that there is no change, $H_0$:
      $\mu_D = 0$.    For these data, s = 5, the standard error is
      1.25, and t(15) = 2.56.    The critical region consists
      of t values beyond ±2.131.    Reject $H_0$ and conclude that
      there has been a significant change in the number of
      cigarettes.

6.    s = 12, t(15) = 3.10.    With $\alpha$ = .01 the critical
      boundary are t = +2.602.    Reject $H_0$ and conclude that
      computerized instruction has a significant effect.

7.    s = 18, standard error is 4.65, and t(14) = −2.75.
      With a one-tailed test at $\alpha$ = .01 the critical boundary
      is t = −2.624.    Reject $H_0$ and conclude that the drug
      significantly reduced blood pressure.

8.    The null hypothesis says that there is no difference
      between the two types of words, $H_0$: $\mu_D = 0$.    For these
      data, s = 6, the standard error is 1, and t(35) = 6.30.
      With $\alpha$ = .01 the critical region consists of t values
      beyond ±2.750.    Reject $H_0$ and conclude that there has
      been a significant difference in recall for pleasant
      versus unpleasant words.

9.   The null hypothesis says that there is no change in the number of dreams, $H_0$: $\mu_D = 0$. For these data, $s = 2$, the standard error is 0.50, and $t(15) = 8.60$. With $\alpha = .05$ the critical region consists of t values beyond $\pm 2.131$. Reject $H_0$ and conclude that there has been a significant change.

10.  The null hypothesis says that there is no increase in gas mileage, $H_0$: $\mu_D \leq 0$. For these data the standard error is 0.44 and $t(9) = 6.14$. For a one-tailed test with $\alpha = .05$ the critical region consists of t values beyond 1.833. Reject $H_0$ and conclude that there has been a significant increase in mileage.

11.  The null hypothesis says that there is no increase in pain tolerance, $H_0$: $\mu_D \leq 0$. For these data, $s = 8$, the standard error is 2, and $t(15) = 5.25$. For a one-tailed test with $\alpha = .01$ the critical region consists of t values beyond 2.602. Reject $H_0$ and conclude that there has been a significant increase in pain tolerance.

12.  The null hypothesis says that there is no difference between the two food mixes, $H_0$: $\mu_D = 0$. For these data, $s = 6$, the standard error is 2, and $t(8) = 3.00$. With $\alpha = .05$ the critical region consists of t values beyond $\pm 2.306$. Reject $H_0$ and conclude that there has been a significant difference between the two food mixes.

13.  a. The null hypothesis states that there is no difference between the two treatments, $H_0$: $\mu_1 - \mu_2 = 0$. The pooled variance is 35.5, the standard error is 3.77, and $t(8) = 0.53$. Fail to reject $H_0$. There is no significant difference between the two treatments.

b.  For the repeated-measures design, $H_0: \mu_D = 0$.  For these data, s = 1, the standard error is 0.45, and t(4) = 4.44.  With $\alpha$ = .05 the critical region consists of t values beyond ±2.776.  Reject $H_0$ and conclude that there is a significant difference between treatments.

c.  The repeated-measures design has less variability and a smaller standard error.  The smaller standard error results in a larger t statistic which is big enough to be significant.

14. The null hypothesis says that there is no difference between shots shots fired during versus between heart beats, $H_0: \mu_D = 0$.  For these data, $\bar{D}$ = 2.83, SS = 34.83, s = 2.64, the standard error is 1.08, and t(5) = 2.62.  With $\alpha$ = .05 the critical region consists of t values beyond ±2.571.  Reject $H_0$ and conclude that the timing of the shot has a significant effect on the marksmen's scores.

15. The null hypothesis says that deprivation has no effect on hearing threshold, $H_0: \mu_D = 0$.  For these data, $\bar{D}$ = −2.29, SS = 51.43, s = 2.93, the standard error is 1.11, and t(6) = −2.06.  With $\alpha$ = .05 the critical region consists of t values beyond ±2.447.  Fail to reject $H_0$ and conclude that the data show no significant change in hearing threshold.

16. The null hypothesis says that there is no difference between the two stores, $H_0: \mu_D = 0$.  For these data, $\bar{D}$ = −0.08, SS = .1334, s = 0.129, the standard error is 0.043, and t(8) = −1.86.  With $\alpha$ = .05 the critical region consists of t values beyond ±2.306.  Fail to reject $H_0$ and conclude that the data show no significant difference in prices between the two stores.

17. $H_0$: $\mu_D \geq 0$ (no decrease) For these data, $\bar{D}$ = -4.20, s = 2.95, the standard error is 1.32, and t(4) = -3.18. For a one tailed test with $\alpha$ = .05 the critical boundary is t = -2.132. Reject $H_0$ and conclude that the treatment significantly reduces nightmares.

18. $H_0$: $\mu_D \geq 0$ (no decrease) For these data, $\bar{D}$ = -2.125, s = 10.29, the standard error is 3.64, and t(7) = -0.58. Fail to reject $H_0$ and conclude that hypnosis had no significant effect on weight loss.

19. For the difference scores, $\bar{D}$ = 2.71, SS = 49.43, s = 2.87, the standard error is 1.08, and t(6) = 2.51. The critical boundaries are t = ±2.447. Reject $H_0$ and conclude that there is a significant difference in fitness between walkers and drivers.

20. For these data $\bar{D}$ = 0.90, s = 0.74, the standard error is 0.22, and t(10) = 4.09. For a one-tailed test with $\alpha$ = .05 the critical value is t = 1.812. Reject $H_0$ and conclude that the drug has a significant effect.

# CHAPTER 12: ESTIMATION

1.  The general purpose of a hypothesis test is to determine whether or not a treatment effect exists. A hypothesis test always addresses a "yes/no" question. The purpose of estimation is to determine the size of the effect. Estimation addresses a "how much" question.

2.  If a hypothesis test results in failure to reject $H_0$, the conclusion is that there is no significant treatment effect. In this case it would be pointless to attempt to determine the size of the effect.

3.  a.  The larger the sample, the narrower the interval.
    b.  The larger the sample standard deviation (s), the wider the interval.
    c.  The higher the percentage of confidence, the wider the interval.

4.  a.  With two separate samples, use an independent measures t statistic to estimate how much difference there is between the review course and control conditions.
    b.  This is a repeated measures hypothesis testing situation. The researcher wants to determine whether or not the medication is effective.

5.  a.  Use the sample mean, $\bar{X}$ = 5.1 hours, as the best point estimate of $\mu$.
    b.  0.4 hours

c. With a standard error of 0.20 and z-scores ranging from -1.28 to +1.28 for 80% confidence, the interval extends from 4.844 hours to 5.356 hours.

6. The width of the interval depends on standard error which varies inversely with the square root of n. To decrease the interval width by a factor of 2, you must increase the sample size by a factor of 4: from n = 25 to n = 100.

7. a. Use $\bar{X}$ = 820 for the point estimate.
   b. Using z = ±1.28, the 80% confidence interval extends from 817.44 to 822.56.
   c. Using z = ±2.58, the 99% confidence interval extends from 814.84 to 825.16.

8. a. Use $\bar{X}$ = 31 minutes for the point estimate.
   b. With df = 8 the t values for 95% confidence are t = ±2.306. The estimated standard error is 3, and the 95% confidence interval extends from 24.082 to 37.918.

9. a. s = 2.91
   b. Use $\bar{X}$ = 10.09 for the point estimate. Using t = ±2.228 and a standard error of 0.88, the 95% confidence interval extends from 8.13 to 12.05.

10. a. s = 10
    b. Use $\bar{X}$ = 43 to estimate $\mu$.
    c. Using t = ±1.711, estimate $\mu$ between 39.578 and 46.422.

11. a. Use $\bar{X}$ = 95 for the boys. With a standard error of 3 and using a range of t values from -1.341 to 1.341, the interval extends from 90.977 to 99.023.

b.  Use $\bar{X}$ = 40 for the girls.  With a standard error of 4 and using a range of t values from -1.397 to 1.397, the interval extends from 34.412 to 45.588.

c.  Use the sample mean difference, 45 millimeters, for the point estimate.  Using an independent-measures t statistic with df = 23, the pooled variance is 144, the standard error is 5, the t score boundaries for 80% confidence are ±1.319, and the interval extends from 38.405 to 51.595.

12.  Use the sample mean difference, 5.5, for the point estimate.  Using a repeated-measures t statistic with df = 15, the standard error is 2, the t score boundaries for 80% confidence are ±1.341, and the interval extends from 2.818 to 8.182.

13.  Use the sample mean difference, 14 points, for the point estimate.  Using an independent-measures t statistic with df = 28, the pooled variance is 120, the standard error is 4, the t score boundaries for 90% confidence are ±1.701, and the interval extends from 7.196 to 20.804.

14.  Use the sample mean difference, 0.72, for the point estimate.  Using a repeated-measures t statistic with df = 24, the standard error is 0.20, the t score boundaries for 95% confidence are ±2.064, and the interval extends from 0.3072 to 1.1328.

15.  Use the sample mean difference, 8 minutes, for the point estimate.  Using a repeated-measures t statistic with df = 8, the standard error is 2, the t score boundaries for 80% confidence are ±1.397, and the interval extends from 5.206 to 10.794 minutes.

16. Use the sample mean difference, 12 points, for the point estimate. Using an independent-measures t statistic with df = 48, the pooled variance is 50, the standard error is 2, the t score boundaries for 90% confidence are ±1.684, and the interval extends from 8.632 to 15.368.

17. Use the sample mean difference, 4.2, for the point estimate. Using a repeated-measures t statistic with df = 3, the standard error is 1, the t score boundaries for 95% confidence are ±3.182, and the interval extends from 1.018 to 7.382.

18. Use the sample mean difference, 3.928 points, for the point estimate. Using an independent-measures t statistic with df = 26, the pooled variance is 2.485, the standard error is 0.595, the t score boundaries for 90% confidence are ±1.706, and the interval extends from 2.913 to 4.943.

19. Use the sample mean difference, 2.83, for the point estimate. Using a repeated-measures t statistic with df = 5, the standard error is 1.08, the t score boundaries for 80% confidence are ±1.476, and the interval extends from 1.236 to 4.424.

20. a. Use $\bar{X}$ = 46.48 for the point estimate of $\mu$.
    b. With a standard error of 1.29 and t = ±2.086, the 95% confidence interval extends from 43.79 to 49.17.
    c. Yes. The mean for 6-year-olds is $\mu$ = 50. This value is greater than the estimated mean for 5-year-olds (confidence interval).

# CHAPTER 13: INTRODUCTION TO ANALYSIS OF VARIANCE

1. When there is no treatment effect, the numerator and the denominator of the F-ratio are both measuring the same sources of variability (individual differences and experimental error). In this case, the F-ratio is balanced and should have a value near 1.00.

2. Both the F-ratio and the t statistic are comparing the actual mean difference between samples (numerator) with the difference that would be expected from chance factors such as experimental error (denominator). If the numerator is sufficiently bigger than the denominator, we conclude that there is a significant difference between treatments.

3. With 3 or more treatment conditions you need 2 or more t tests to evaluate all the mean differences. Each test involves a risk of a Type I error. The more tests you do the more risk there is of a Type I error. The ANOVA performs all of the tests simultaneously with a single, fixed alpha level.

4. Post tests are done after an ANOVA where you reject the null hypothesis with 3 or more treatments. Post tests determine which treatments are significantly different.

5. a. There is no difference between treatments: Both have $T = 8$ and $\bar{X} = 2$. $MS_{between}$ should be zero.
   b. $F = 0$
   c. $SS_{between} = 0$ and $MS_{between} = 0$

6.   Within each treatment all the scores are the same.
There is no variability within treatments.  $MS_{within}$
should be zero.

7.

| Source | SS | df | MS | |
|---|---|---|---|---|
| Between Treatments | 10 | 2 | 5.00 | $F(2,12) = 3.75$ |
| Within Treatments | 16 | 12 | 1.33 | |
| Total | 26 | 14 | | |

The critical value is $F = 3.88$.  Fail to reject $H_0$.
These data do not provide evidence of any differences
among the three therapies.

8.   a.   SS = 26
b.   For the first column, SS = 14.   For the second
column, SS = 10.
c.   $T_1 = 8$ and $T_2 = 12$.   $SS_{between} = 2$

9.   a.

| Source | SS | df | MS | |
|---|---|---|---|---|
| Between Treatments | 56 | 2 | 28 | $F(2,9) = 7.00$ |
| Within Treatments | 36 | 9 | 4 | |
| Total | 92 | 11 | | |

With a critical value of $F = 4.26$ you should reject $H_0$
and conclude that there are significant differences
among the three treatments.
b.   For Treatment I versus II, the Scheffe $F(2,9) =$
0.25, not significant.   For treatment II versus III,
Scheffe $F(2,9) = 4.00$, not significant.   For Treatment
I versus III, Scheffe $F(2,9) = 6.25$, which is a
significant difference at the .05 level.

10.  a.

| Source | SS | df | MS | |
|---|---|---|---|---|
| Between Treatments | 36 | 2 | 18 | $F(2,15) = 9.00$ |
| Within Treatments | 30 | 15 | 2 | |
| Total | 66 | 17 | | |

With a critical value of F = 6.36, reject $H_0$.

b. The greatest change in attitude occurs when there is a moderate discrepancy between the persuasive argument and a person's original opinion.

11.

| Number of Days to Adjust to Jetlag | | |
|---|---|---|
| Westbound | $\underline{M}$ = 2.50 | $\underline{SD}$ = 1.05 |
| Eastbound | $\underline{M}$ = 6.00 | $\underline{SD}$ = 1.41 |
| Same Time Zone | $\underline{M}$ = 0.50 | $\underline{SD}$ = 0.55 |

| Source | SS | df | MS | |
|---|---|---|---|---|
| Between Treatments | 93 | 2 | 46.50 | $F_{(2,15)}$ = 41.15 |
| Within Treatments | 17 | 15 | 1.13 | |
| Total | 110 | 17 | | |

With a critical value of F = 3.68 you should reject $H_0$.

12.

| Source | SS | df | MS | |
|---|---|---|---|---|
| Between Treatments | 48 | 2 | 24 | $F_{(2,27)}$ = 12.00 |
| Within Treatments | 54 | 27 | 2 | |
| Total | 102 | 29 | | |

13.

| Source | SS | df | MS | |
|---|---|---|---|---|
| Between Treatments | 45 | 3 | 15 | $F_{(3,36)}$ = 5.00 |
| Within Treatments | 108 | 36 | 3 | |
| Total | 153 | 39 | | |

14.

| Source | SS | df | MS | |
|---|---|---|---|---|
| Between Treatments | 30 | 3 | 10 | $F_{(3,20)}$ = 5.00 |
| Within Treatments | 40 | 20 | 2 | |
| Total | 70 | 23 | | |

15. a.

| Source | SS | df | MS | |
|--------|----|----|----|----|
| Between Treatments | 26 | 2 | 13 | $F_{(2,6)} = 6.50$ |
| Within Treatments | 12 | 6 | 2 | |
| Total | 38 | 8 | | |

With a critical value of $F = 5.14$ you should reject $H_0$ and conclude that there are significant differences among the three age groups.

b. Beginning with the largest difference between samples, the Scheffé comparisons and F-ratios are as follows:

5 versus 7-year-olds: $F_{(2, 6)} = 6.00$ (significant)
6 versus 7-year-olds: $F_{(2, 6)} = 3.38$ (not significant)
No other differences are significant.

16.

| Source | SS | df | MS | |
|--------|----|----|----|----|
| Between Treatments | 649.2 | 3 | 216.4 | $F_{(3,16)} = 54.44$ |
| Within Treatments | 63.6 | 16 | 3.975 | |
| Total | 712.8 | 19 | | |

With a critical value of $F = 3.24$, you should reject $H_0$.

17. a. The treatment means and SS values are:

$\bar{X} = 7.56$        $\bar{X} = 4.22$        $\bar{X} = 6.67$
$SS = 30.22$        $SS = 9.56$        $SS = 36.00$

b.

| Source | SS | df | MS | |
|--------|----|----|----|----|
| Between Treatments | 53.63 | 2 | 26.82 | $F_{(2,24)} = 8.49$ |
| Within Treatments | 75.78 | 24 | 3.16 | |
| Total | 129.41 | 26 | | |

The critical value is $F = 3.40$. Reject $H_0$ and conclude that there are significant differences among the three conditions.

c.   Beginning with the largest mean difference, the Scheffe test results are:

No Instr. versus Images: $F_{(2,24)} = 7.91$ (significant)

Sentences versus Images:  $F_{(2,24)} = 4.25$ (significant)

No Instr. versus Sentences:  $F_{(2,24)} = 0.56$ (not significant)

The imagery condition is significantly different from either of the other two.

d.   The imagery instructions produced significantly better performance than either of the other two conditions.   There was no significant difference between sentences and no instructions.

18.  a.

| Source | SS | df | MS | |
|---|---|---|---|---|
| Between treatments | 30 | 2 | 15 | $F_{(2,12)} = 15.00$ |
| Within Treatments | 12 | 12 | 1 | |
| Total | 42 | 14 | | |

The critical value is $F = 3.88$.   Reject $H_0$ and conclude that there are significant differences among the three groups.

b.   Of the three samples the largest variance is for the right-handed subjects ($s^2 = 1.50$) and the smallest is for the left-handed subjects ($s^2 = 0.50$).   F-max = 3.00 which is not significant.   The homogeneity assumption is satisfied.

19.  a.   The means and SS values are:

| Alphas | Betas | Gammas |
|---|---|---|
| $\bar{X} = 44.2$ | $\bar{X} = 47.1$ | $\bar{X} = 36.8$ |
| SS = 865.6 | SS = 500.9 | SS = 325.6 |

The analysis of variance produces,

| Source | SS | df | MS | |
|---|---|---|---|---|
| Between Treatments | 564.2 | 2 | 282.10 | $F_{(2,27)} = 4.50$ |
| Within Treatments | 1692.1 | 27 | 62.67 | |
| Total | 2256.3 | 29 | | |

The critical value is F = 3.35. Reject $H_0$. There are significant differences among the three groups.

b. Beginning with the largest mean difference, the Scheffé test results are:

Betas versus Gammas: $F_{(2,27)} = 4.23$ (significant)

Alphas versus Gammas: $F_{(2,27)} = 2.18$ (not significant)

The only significant difference is between the Betas and the Gammas. The Alphas are an intermediate group, not significantly different from either extreme.

20. a. The means and SS values for these data are

| Attractive | Average | Unattractive |
|---|---|---|
| $\overline{X} = 4.50$ | $\overline{X} = 5.92$ | $\overline{X} = 2.33$ |
| SS = 23.00 | SS = 24.92 | SS = 12.67 |

b.

| Source | SS | df | MS | |
|---|---|---|---|---|
| Between Treatments | 78.17 | 2 | 39.08 | $F_{(2,33)} = 21.24$ |
| Within Treatments | 60.59 | 33 | 1.84 | |
| Total | 138.76 | 35 | | |

The critical value is F = 3.30. Reject $H_0$.

c. Beginning with the largest differnce between samples, the Scheffé comparisons and F-ratios are as follows:

Average vs Unattract. $F_{(2, 33)} = 20.94$ (significant)

Attract vs Unattract. $F_{(2, 33)} = 7.65$ (significant)

Attract vs Average $F_{(2, 33)} = 3.27$ (not significant)

d. An average appearance produces the highest job rating. Individuals who are too attractive or too unattractive are rated lower, although the difference between average and attractive was not significant.

# CHAPTER 14: CORRELATION AND REGRESSION

1.     Set I SP = 6; Set II SP = -16; Set III SP = -4

2.     a.

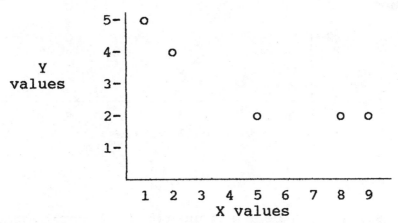

    b.   Estimate a strong negative correlation, probably r = -.8 or -.9.

    c.   $SS_x = 50$, $SS_y = 8$, SP = -18, and r = -.90.

3.     a.

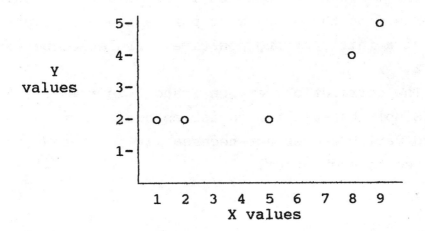

    b.   Estimate a strong positive correlation, probably +.8 or +.9.

c.  $SS_X = 50$, $SS_Y = 8$, $SP = 18$.  $r = +0.90$.

4.   a.

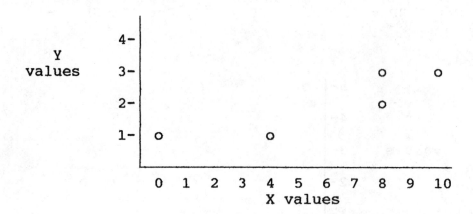

b.  It appears to be a strong positive correlation, about $r = +.8$ or $+.9$.

c.  $SS_X = 64$, $SS_Y = 4$, $SP = 14$, and $r = +.875$

d.  $SS_X = 64$, $SS_Y = 14$, $SP = -16$, and $r = -.535$

5.   a.  The correlation between X and Y is $r = +0.60$.

b.  The correlation between Y and Z is $r = +0.60$.

c.  Based on the answers to part a and part b you might expect a fairly strong positive correlation between X and Z.

d.  The correlation between X and Z is $r = -.20$.

e.  Simply because two variables are both related to a third variable does not necessarily imply that they are related to each other.

6.  a.

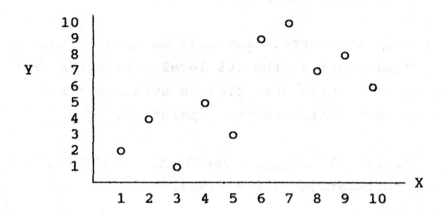

b.  r = 0.697

c.  r = 0.30

d.  r = -0.80

e.  The correlations for parts c and d were computed for a restricted range of scores and do not accurately represent the full range of X and Y values.


7.  a.  $SS_x$ = 63.5, $SS_y$ = 50.875, SP = -51.25, and r = -.902.

b.  The correlation is still r = -.902

c.  Adding a constant does not change $SS_x$ or SP or the correlation.

d.  The correlation is still r = -.902.

e.  Multiplying each score by 3 will cause all the $SS_x$ and SP values to be multiplied by 9.  However, this multiplication cancels out in the correlation formula, so the correlation is unchanged.


8.  $SS_x$ = 12.8, $SS_y$ = 22.8, SP = 6.2.  r = +0.36.


9.  For these data, $SS_{wife}$ = 211.50, $SS_{husband}$ = 137.87, SP = 155.25, and the Pearson correlation is r = 0.909.  With df = 6, the correlation is significant at the .05 level.

10. For these data, $SS_{anxiety} = 18$, $SS_{exam} = 72$, $SP = -32$, and the Pearson correlation is $r = -0.889$.

11. With $n = 25$ the correlation must be greater than 0.396 to be significant at the .05 level. Reject $H_0$ and conclude that these data provide evidence for a non-zero correlation in the population.

12. $SS_{LCU} = 72,104.18$, $SS_{visits} = 96.73$, $SP = 2473.64$, and the Pearson correlation is $r = 0.937$.

13. a. $SS_{RT} = 3023.88$, $SS_{errors} = 89.88$, $SP = -402.88$, and the Pearson correlation is $r = -0.773$.
    b. There is a consistent, negative relation between reaction time and errors. As reaction time gets faster (shorter time), errors increase.

14.

$Y = 3X - 2$

15. a. For company A, $Y = 6X + 10$. For company B, $Y = 5X + 20$.
    b. For company A the cost is $70, and for company B the cost is $70.

c.  An order of 20 rats would be less money from company B ($120 versus $130).

16.  $SS_x = 20$, $SS_y = 24$, $SP = -20$.  The regression equation is  $\hat{Y} = (-1)X + 10$

17.  a.  $\hat{Y} = 3X - 3$
    b.  For each X, the predicted Y value would be,

| X | $\hat{Y}$ |
|---|---|
| 1 | 0 |
| 4 | 9 |
| 3 | 6 |
| 2 | 3 |
| 5 | 12 |
| 3 | 6 |

18.  $SS_x = 10$, $SS_y = 67.2$, $SP = 24$, $r = +0.926$.  The regression equation is, $\hat{Y} = 2.4X + 6.8$.

19.  $\hat{Y} = 36.8X + 395$

20.  a.  $\hat{Y} = 2X + 13$
    b.  The slope (b = 2) indicates an additional salary of $2000 for each additional year of higher education.
    c.  The Y-intercept (a = 13) indicates that the predicted salary for an individual with no higher education (X = 0) is 13 thousand dollars.

21.  a.  $SS_x = 224.88$, $SS_y = 880.87$, $SP = 400.88$, $r = +0.901$
    b.  With n = 8 and $\alpha = .05$, the critical value is 0.707.  Reject $H_0$ and conclude that there is a significant relationship.
    c.  The regression equation is $\hat{Y} = 1.78X + 191.47$.  For X = 20 thousand, $\hat{Y} = 227.07$ thousand.

22.  a.  $SS_{temp} = 999.60$, $SS_{crime} = 20.50$, $SP = 122$, and the Pearson correlation is $r = 0.852$.

b.  The data indicate a tendency for violent crimes to increase as the temperature goes up.

c.  The regression equation is $\hat{Y} = 0.122X - 3.53$, where $\hat{Y}$ is the predicted number of crimes and X is the temperature.

# CHAPTER 15: THE CHI-SQUARE STATISTIC: TESTS FOR GOODNESS OF FIT AND INDEPENDENCE

1.  $H_0$: The four factors are equally important, p = 0.25 for each factor. The expected frequency is 25 for all four categories. Chi-square = 20. With df = 3 the critical value is 7.81. Reject $H_0$ and conclude that the four factors are not equally important.

2.  $H_0$ states that the distribution of flu related deaths is the same as the distribution of the population: 30% under 30, 40% for 30 to 60, and 30% for over 60. The expected frequencies for these three categories are 15, 20, and 15. Chi-square = 59.58. With df = 2, the critical value is 5.99. Reject $H_0$ and conclude that the distribution of flu-related deaths is not identical to the population distribution.

3.  The chi-square test requires that each observed frequency represent a separate and independent observation. Usually this requires that each individual be counted once and only once. For example, a sample of n = 20 observations usually requires a sample of n = 20 individuals. In this problem the same rat is observed over and over again, and it is not reasonable to assume that the different observations are independent.

4.   a.  $H_0$: The population proportions have not changed
     and are still 30% science, 50% social science or
     humanities, and 20% professional.  The expected
     frequencies for these three categories are 30, 50, and
     20 respectively.  Chi-square = 4.08.  With df = 2, the
     critical value is 5.99.  Fail to reject $H_0$ and conclude
     that there has been no significant change in freshman
     majors.
     b.  With n = 200, Chi-square = 8.16.  Reject $H_0$.
     c.  A larger sample should be more representative of
     the population.  If the sample continues to be
     different from the hypothesis as n increases, the
     difference eventually will be significant.

5.   The null hypothesis states that there is no preference
     among the three photographs;  p = 1/3 for all
     categories.  The expected frequencies are $f_e$ = 50 for
     all categories, and chi-square = 20.28.  With df = 2,
     the critical value is 5.99.  Reject $H_0$ and conclude
     that there are significant preferences.

6.   The null hypothesis states that there are no
     differences in relapse response (relapse vs. no
     relapse) among the three drugs.  The expected
     frequencies among those that relapsed are $f_e$ = 12 for
     all drug categories.  For those that did not relapse,
     $f_e$ = 18 for all drug categories.  Chi-square = 14.44.
     With df = 2 the critical value is 5.99.  You should
     reject $H_0$ and conclude that there is a relationship
     between drug condition and relapse response.

7.  The null hypothesis states that the distribution of blood types in the foreign country is the same as in the United States. The expected frequencies are:

| Type O | Type A | Type B | Type AB |
|--------|--------|--------|---------|
| 61.20 | 55.76 | 13.60 | 5.44 |

Chi-square = 79.74. With df = 3, the critical value is 7.81. Reject $H_0$.

8.  The null hypothesis states that opinions have not changed since 1970 so the distribution should still be 15% for, 79% against, and 6% no opinion. Chi-square = 2.30. With df = 2, the critical value is 5.99. Fail to reject $H_0$. These data do not provide evidence for a change in opinion.

9.  The null hypothesis states that there are no preferences among the five restaurants; p = 1/5 for all categories. The expected frequencies are $f_e$ = 20 for all categories, and chi-square = 19.40. With df = 4, the critical value is 9.49. Reject $H_0$ and conclude that there are significant preferences.

10. The null hypothesis states that there is no relation between dream content and gender; the distribution of aggression content should be the same for males and females. The expected frequencies are:

|        | Low  | Medium | High |
|--------|------|--------|------|
| Female | 8.8  | 8.4    | 6.8  |
| Male   | 13.2 | 12.6   | 10.2 |

The chi-square statistic is 25.52. The critical value is 9.21. Reject $H_0$ with $\alpha$ = .01 and df = 2.

11. The null hypothesis states that there is no relation between handedness and eye preference. The expected frequencies for left handed subjects are 12 left eye and 18 right eye. For right handed subjects the expected frequencies are 48 for left eye and 72 for right eye. Chi-square = 11.11. With df = 1 and $\alpha$ = .01 the critical value is 6.63. There is a significant relation between hand and eye preference.

12. a. The Pearson correlation would require an IQ score and a vocabulary score for each child. The correlation would measure the degree of relationship between the two variables.

    b. The chi-square test would require that each child be classified in terms of IQ (for example, high, medium, or low), and classified in terms of vocabulary skill (good, medium, or poor). The chi-square test would determine whether the frequency distribution for vocabulary was dependent on IQ.

13. The null hypothesis states that there is no relation between education and opinion. The expected frequencies are:

| | For | Against | Undecided |
|---|---|---|---|
| No degree | 25 | 15 | 60 |
| High School | 10 | 6 | 24 |
| College | 15 | 9 | 36 |

Chi-square = 44.03. With df = 4, the critical value is 9.49. Reject $H_0$.

14. The null hypothesis states that the distribution of votes is independent of political party. The expected frequencies for Democrats are 25.2 Yes and 19.8 No. For Republicans, the expected frequencies are 30.8 Yes and 24.2 No. Chi-square = 6.30. With df = 1, the critical value is 3.84. Reject $H_0$ and conclude that there is a significant relation between vote and party affiliation.

15. The null hypothesis states that there is no relation between gender and college major. The expected frequencies are:

|  | Science | Humanities | Arts | Professional |
|---|---|---|---|---|
| Male | 22 | 26 | 12 | 40 |
| Female | 88 | 104 | 48 | 160 |

Chi-square = 17.66. With df = 3 and $\alpha$ = .01 the critical value is 11.34. Reject $H_0$.

16. The null hypothesis states that there is no relation between the tendency to litter and the amount of litter already on the ground. The expected frequencies are $f_e$ = 11.75 for littering and $f_e$ = 38.25 for not littering across all categories. With df = 3, chi-square = 12.99. The critical value is 7.81. Reject $H_0$.

17. The null hypothesis states that there is no relation between personality and heart disease. The expected frequencies are:

|  | Heart | Vascular | Hypertension | None |
|---|---|---|---|---|
| Type A | 27.20 | 24.77 | 27.69 | 90.34 |
| Type B | 28.80 | 26.23 | 29.31 | 95.66 |

Chi-square = 46.03. With df = 3, the critical value is 7.81. Reject $H_0$.

18. The null hypothesis states that the distribution of returned versus not-returned surveys should be the same for the student and the vice president signatures. The expected frequencies show 19.5 surveys returned and 30.5 discarded for both signatures. With df = 1, chi-square is 12.15. With $\alpha$ = .01, the critical value is 6.63. Reject $H_0$ and conclude that the signature on the letter does affect response rate.

19. The null hypothesis states that the distribution of salaries is the same for males and females. The expected frequencies are:

|         | under $20,000 | 20,000-40,000 | over $40,000 |
|---------|---------------|---------------|--------------|
| Males   | 23.6          | 40.4          | 16           |
| Females | 35.4          | 60.6          | 24           |

With df = 2, chi-square = 21.75. The critical value is 5.99. Reject the null hypothesis and conclude that there is a significant difference between the two salary distributions.

20. The null hypothesis states that there is no relation between need for achievement and risk. The expected frequencies are:

|      | Cautious | Moderate | High  |
|------|----------|----------|-------|
| High | 12.18    | 15.10    | 10.72 |
| Low  | 12.82    | 15.90    | 11.28 |

Chi-square = 17.07. With df = 2, the critical value is 5.99. Reject $H_0$.

21. The null hypothesis states that an individual's preferred situation is independent of self-esteem. The expected frequencies are:

|  | Audience | No Audience |
|---|---|---|
| Low | 10 | 10 |
| Medium | 14 | 14 |
| High | 12 | 12 |

Chi-square = 13.2. With df = 2, the critical value is 5.99. Reject $H_0$.

# CHAPTER 16: INTRODUCTION TO MINITAB

**1.**
```
MTB > HISTOGRAM C1
Histogram of C1    N = 30
Midpoint    Count
      10        7   *******
      20        3   ***
      30        4   ****
      40        2   **
      50        2   **
      60        5   *****
      70        4   ****
      80        3   ***
```

```
MTB > DOTPLOT C1
```

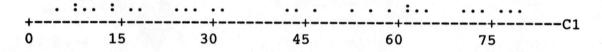

**2.**
```
MTB > DESCRIBE C1
```

|     | N  | MEAN  | MEDIAN | TRMEAN | STDEV | SEMEAN |
|-----|----|-------|--------|--------|-------|--------|
| C1  | 30 | 41.20 | 42.50  | 41.00  | 25.24 | 4.61   |

|     | MIN  | MAX   | Q1    | Q3    |
|-----|------|-------|-------|-------|
| C1  | 5.00 | 79.00 | 15.50 | 63.50 |

**3.**
```
MTB > TTEST 52 C1
```

TEST OF MU = 52.000 VS MU N.E. 52.000

|     | N  | MEAN   | STDEV  | SE MEAN | T     | P VALUE |
|-----|----|--------|--------|---------|-------|---------|
| C1  | 30 | 41.200 | 25.243 | 4.609   | -2.34 | 0.026   |

4.
MTB > TINTERVAL 90 C1

```
        N      MEAN     STDEV    SE MEAN    90.0 PERCENT C.I.
C1      30     41.20    25.24      4.61    (   33.37,    49.03)
```

5.
MTB > DESCRIBE 'BAC' 'RT'

```
             N      MEAN    MEDIAN    TRMEAN     STDEV    SEMEAN
BAC         14    0.0707    0.0650    0.0700    0.0471    0.0126
RT          14    231.21    232.50    232.00     21.01      5.62

           MIN       MAX        Q1        Q3
BAC     0.0000    0.1500    0.0375    0.1050
RT      190.00    263.00    213.25    250.75
```

6.
MTB > PLOT 'RT' 'BAC'

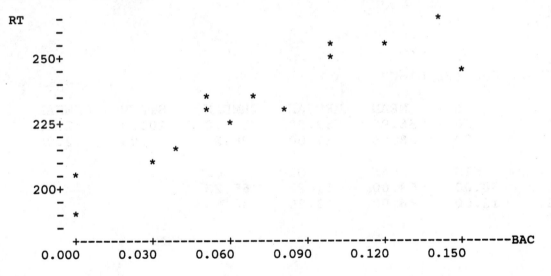

7.
MTB > CORRELATION 'BAC' 'RT'

Correlation of BAC and RT = 0.915

8.
```
MTB > REGRESS 'RT' 1 'BAC'

The regression equation is
RT = 202 + 408 BAC

Predictor         Coef        Stdev     t-ratio         P
Constant       202.388        4.370       46.31     0.000
BAC            407.64         51.99        7.84     0.000

s = 8.838        R-sq = 83.7%      R-sq(adj) = 82.3%

Analysis of Variance

SOURCE          DF          SS           MS          F          P
Regression       1       4801.1       4801.1      61.47     0.000
Error           12        937.2         78.1
Total           13       5738.4

Unusual Observations
Obs.       BAC        RT       Fit Stdev.Fit  Residual   St.Resid
   4     0.150    244.00    263.53      4.75    -19.53     -2.62R

R denotes an obs. with a large st. resid.
```

9.
```
MTB > DESCRIBE C1 C2

            N      MEAN    MEDIAN    TRMEAN     STDEV    SEMEAN
C1         20     56.90     59.50     57.78     10.38      2.32
C2         20     28.85     27.00     28.28     12.99      2.90

          MIN       MAX        Q1        Q3
C1      30.00     68.00     51.25     65.25
C2      12.00     56.00     18.25     38.50
```

10.
```
MTB > DOTPLOT C1 C2

  .            .        .       .    ...        .:  .. .:    . ::
--------+---------+---------+---------+---------+---------+-C1
     35.0      42.0      49.0      56.0      63.0      70.0

  .  ...   ....     .   :       :    . .  .     . . .        .
-----+---------+---------+---------+---------+---------+-C2
  16.0      24.0      32.0      40.0      48.0      56.0
```

11.
```
MTB > TWOSAMPLE C1 C2;
SUBC> POOLED.

TWOSAMPLE T FOR C1 VS C2
             N      MEAN     STDEV    SE MEAN
C1          20      56.9     10.4       2.3
C2          20      28.9     13.0       2.9

95 PCT CI FOR MU C1 - MU C2: (20.5, 35.6)

TTEST MU C1 = MU C2 (VS NE): T= 7.54   P = 0.0000   DF=  38
POOLED STDEV =           11.8
```

12.
```
MTB > AOVONEWAY C1 C2

ANALYSIS OF VARIANCE
SOURCE      DF        SS        MS        F          P
FACTOR       1      7868      7868      56.92      0.000
ERROR       38      5252       138
TOTAL       39     13120
                                   INDIVIDUAL 95 PCT CI'S FOR MEAN
                                   BASED ON POOLED STDEV
LEVEL       N      MEAN     STDEV   --+---------+---------+---------+----
C1          20     56.90    10.38                         (---*----)
C2          20     28.85    12.99      (---*---)
                                   --+---------+---------+---------+----
POOLED STDEV =     11.76            24        36        48        60
```

13.
```
MTB> HISTOGRAM C1 C2

Histogram of BEFORE    N = 12

Midpoint    Count
      35        1    *
      40        1    *
      45        1    *
      50        2    **
      55        3    ***
      60        1    *
      65        0
      70        2    **
      75        0
      80        0
      85        0
      90        1    *
```

```
Histogram of AFTER    N = 12

Midpoint    Count
     40        1    *
     45        0
     50        0
     55        0
     60        1    *
     65        2    **
     70        0
     75        3    ***
     80        2    **
     85        1    *
     90        2    **
```

14.
MTB > DESCRIBE C1 C2

|        | N  | MEAN  | MEDIAN | TRMEAN | STDEV | SEMEAN |
|--------|----|-------|--------|--------|-------|--------|
| BEFORE | 12 | 56.33 | 53.00  | 55.30  | 14.86 | 4.29   |
| AFTER  | 12 | 73.17 | 76.00  | 74.90  | 14.73 | 4.25   |

|        | MIN   | MAX   | Q1    | Q3    |
|--------|-------|-------|-------|-------|
| BEFORE | 35.00 | 88.00 | 47.00 | 68.50 |
| AFTER  | 39.00 | 90.00 | 64.25 | 84.25 |

15.
MTB > LET C3 = C2 - C1
MTB > TTEST 0 C3

TEST OF MU = 0.000 VS MU N.E.   0.000

|    | N  | MEAN   | STDEV  | SE MEAN | T    | P VALUE |
|----|----|--------|--------|---------|------|---------|
| C3 | 12 | 16.833 | 17.130 | 4.945   | 3.40 | 0.0059  |

16.
MTB > LET C3 = C2 - C1
MTB > TINTERVAL 80 C3

|    | N  | MEAN  | STDEV | SE MEAN | 80.0 PERCENT C.I. |
|----|----|-------|-------|---------|-------------------|
| C3 | 12 | 16.83 | 17.13 | 4.94    | ( 10.09, 23.58)   |

**17.**
```
MTB > DESCRIBE C1-C4
```

|          | N  | MEAN  | MEDIAN | TRMEAN | STDEV | SEMEAN |
|----------|----|-------|--------|--------|-------|--------|
| CONTROL  | 10 | 14.70 | 15.00  | 14.75  | 3.59  | 1.14   |
| TRTMNT A | 10 | 21.40 | 23.50  | 21.75  | 6.64  | 2.10   |
| TRTMNT B | 10 | 10.10 | 7.50   | 9.75   | 5.95  | 1.88   |
| TRTMNT C | 10 | 27.30 | 28.00  | 27.38  | 8.46  | 2.68   |

|          | MIN   | MAX   | Q1    | Q3    |
|----------|-------|-------|-------|-------|
| CONTROL  | 9.00  | 20.00 | 11.75 | 18.00 |
| TRTMNT A | 10.00 | 30.00 | 14.75 | 26.50 |
| TRTMNT B | 3.00  | 20.00 | 5.75  | 16.00 |
| TRTMNT C | 15.00 | 39.00 | 20.00 | 34.25 |

**18.**
```
MTB > DOTPLOT C1-C4
```

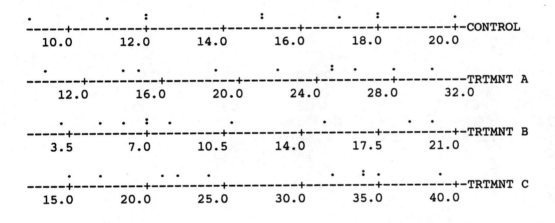

19.
MTB > AOVONEWAY C1-C4

ANALYSIS OF VARIANCE

| SOURCE | DF | SS | MS | F | P |
|--------|-----|--------|-------|-------|-------|
| FACTOR | 3 | 1707.9 | 569.3 | 13.89 | 0.000 |
| ERROR | 36 | 1475.5 | 41.0 | | |
| TOTAL | 39 | 3183.4 | | | |

```
                                    INDIVIDUAL 95 PCT CI'S FOR MEAN
                                    BASED ON POOLED STDEV
LEVEL       N      MEAN    STDEV   --+---------+---------+---------+----
CONTROL    10     14.700   3.592            (-----*-----)
TRTMNT A   10     21.400   6.637                       (-----*----)
TRTMNT B   10     10.100   5.953    (----*-----)
TRTMNT C   10     27.300   8.460                                (-----*-----)
                                    --+---------+---------+---------+----
POOLED STDEV =     6.402            7.0      14.0      21.0      28.0
```

20.
MTB > READ C1-C3
DATA> 12   5   3
DATA>  5   6  14
DATA> END
      2 ROWS READ
MTB > CHISQUARE C1-C3

Expected counts are printed below observed counts

|       | C1    | C2    | C3    | Total |
|-------|-------|-------|-------|-------|
| 1     | 12    | 5     | 3     | 20    |
|       | 7.56  | 4.89  | 7.56  |       |
| 2     | 5     | 6     | 14    | 25    |
|       | 9.44  | 6.11  | 9.44  |       |
| Total | 17    | 11    | 17    | 45    |

ChiSq = 2.614 + 0.003 + 2.747 +
        2.092 + 0.002 + 2.197 = 9.655
df = 2
1 cells with expected counts less than 5.0